David Wilkerson

Contents

CHAPTER ONE

In the headlines

`Judge Davidson. I'd like to speak to you. I'm a minister of religion.'

The skinny man from the spectator section strode towards the judge, who was now on his feet and getting ready to leave the crowded courtroom.

Judge Davidson was surprised to hear a country accent in a New York courtroom. But out-of-town or not, he was taking no chances on this stranger. Not after he'd received threats to his own life. The defendants in this case might only be teenage boys but they were up on a murder charge – and they had dangerous friends.

`Get this man out of here,' the judge snarled, a glint of fear in his eyes.

Even as he spoke, two guards scrabbled towards the man, and grabbed him roughly. It didn't take much of an effort for them to restrain their captive, partly because of his slight build and partly because he didn't seem to be struggling very hard.

The minister's gaze followed the judge as he gathered up his robes and left the courtroom. No chance to talk to him now. He'd failed. He had definitely failed. Now he had no way of helping those seven boys.

The guards interrupted his thoughts as they roughly searched him.

`Has he got a gun?' one guard asked the other.

`I can't find one on him,' replied his colleague. `He seems clean.'

`Let's get him out of here anyway.'

Together they manhandled him out of the courtroom so fast that his feet hardly touched the ground. A few enterprising pressmen elbowed their way out behind them. There might be a story in this. `Crazed preacher threatens judge's life in courtroom drama.' This was too good a chance to miss.

The skinny man didn't look too dangerous to them, but then a lot of these criminals don't. He looked kind of ordinary – neat and clean, with bewildered blue eyes. You could even feel sorry for him, bundled like a parcel into the vestibule in the custody of two burly police officers.

`Who are you?'

`David Wilkerson.'

`And what were you doing in the courtroom?'

`I only wanted to speak to the judge. About the boys.'

`You a friend of theirs?'

`They don't know me. They've never even met me. But, yes, I want to be their friend.'

Alongside the cops, he was looking pale and tired now. And desperate. It was like some terrible nightmare, but he knew it was true. There was no escaping the situation.

He sighed deeply. He was just a small-town preacher from Pennsylvania. How on earth had he gotten into this mess? Here at a New York murder trial, held by the police as a suspected criminal?

In his mind, David Wilkerson returned to February 9th, 1958, the night when it really all began. That was when he had decided to sell his television. Little did he know at the time where that simple decision was going to lead him.

*   *   *   *   *   *

It had been an ordinary evening. As usual, he was the last one to go to bed, and he was lazing on the couch, trying to unwind with a bit of television. Some dancers in flimsy costumes were doing a fairly typical routine on the *Late Show*, the sort of thing he'd seen thousands of times before. He usually found it pleasant enough to watch, but not tonight.

Tonight it left him cold.

He switched off the television set and went through to his office. Why couldn't he settle? Suddenly it seemed that television was a waste of time. Why did he bother?

He mentally flipped through the old excuses he usually gave. He led a busy life and needed a couple of hours of late night TV to relax. And as a pastor, he had a duty to make himself familiar with what his congregation was watching.

Tonight, however, neither of those reasons

sounded convincing. His wife, Gwen, and their children led busy lives and managed to communicate with the congregation, and they never watched TV. He was the only person in the household who ever switched it on.

Maybe I should go ahead and sell the darned thing? he thought to himself. Just think what could happen if I spent all that extra time in prayer.

Then he hesitated. Was this really necessary? What did it really matter whether he watched television or not? It was no big deal. But in that case, why was he reluctant to give it up?

The preacher had a feeling that there were more than his favourite programmes at stake. He sensed that his life would change, and he wasn't sure what that would involve. Did he really want to take the risk? Wasn't he happy with his life just as it was?

But what if it was God's will? What if God was asking him to give up television and spend more time with Him?

There was only one way to find out. He'd put out a fleece for God. In other words, he'd ask God for a sign, just as Gideon in the Old Testament had done when he laid out a lamb's fleece on the ground; in the morning, if everything was covered in dew except the fleece, Gideon would know what God wanted of him.

`Lord,' said David Wilkerson. `I want to know what it is You require of me. I'll advertise the

4

television set in the paper, and if You really want me to sell it, send me a buyer immediately. Get him to contact me by the time the paper's been on sale for . . . for half an hour.'

The next day he was beginning to think that maybe he'd set God a tough task. Only half an hour. Maybe his wife, Gwen, was right – he'd do anything to avoid all that extra praying.

A few days later, the ad was in the paper and the minutes were ticking by. Half an hour. It would all be settled in half an hour – either way.

After twenty-nine minutes, it looked as if the TV was there to stay. No one had phoned. David was beginning to relax and look forward to more lazy nights in front of the *Late Show*.

`That's nearly it, then,' he said to Gwen.

`Don't count on it,' said Gwen. `The time isn't up yet.'

The telephone's ring jolted David from his seat.

`I'm calling about the television set,' said the man. `You still got it?'

`I sure have,' said David. `It's only two years old, and it's got a nineteen-inch screen.'

`How much?'

David gulped. He hadn't thought this far ahead. `I'll take a hundred dollars for it.'

`Done,' said the man. `Just you wait there. I'll come straight round for it.'

*　　*　　*　　*　　*　　*

Funny to think that that was where it had all started. His visit to New York. His mission from God. And now his arrest. All through his life he'd always known that God was good to him. God answered his prayers, he knew that. And if God wanted him to do something specific, he usually knew that too. Only this time it seemed that he'd got it all wrong. Badly wrong.

`That was some stunt you pulled in there,' said the sergeant. `Let's see what you've got on you.'

`I told you. I don't have a gun.'

He was carefully searched for the second time that morning.

`Who put you up to this then?'

`No one. I just wanted to help those boys.'

`Are you mixed up with the Dragons?'

`Not the way you mean.'

`Any more of you in there?'

`Only Miles Hoover, the youth director of my church. Look, I can explain . . .'

`Is he your backup?'

`It isn't like that . . . I'm a minister . . . Look . . . I'll show you my ordination papers.'

David dug deep into his pocket for the relevant document, no easy task as he was handcuffed to one of the officers.

`Where did you get these from? They must be forged.'

`I'm telling you. They're genuine.'

`Yeah, and I'm Ali Baba.'

6

The security guards pushed open the door again and hustled in another man, none too gently. The man looked angry.

`He's telling the truth,' said the new arrival. `This is the Reverend David Wilkerson. He's the pastor at my church in Philipsburg.'

`Why don't you check out the information?' David suggested, trying to sound authoritative although his voice was coming out weak and strangled.

The sergeant hesitated. He'd heard it all before, but you had to be meticulous in these matters. `What did you say the name of the church was?' He wrote it down in his notebook.

`Keep an eye on these two,' he said as he made his way to the court office.

Not that David and Miles intended going anywhere. They'd had more than their fair share of conflict already. From now on they'd do what they were told to the letter. They weren't taking any more chances.

Held by the police! Treated like common criminals! The shame of it! Whatever would they say when they were back in the parish? Who would believe that the minister had been arrested for disturbing the processes of justice? Especially as he'd told them that it was God who wanted him to come to New York.

David could see that Miles was angry. He couldn't blame him really. Making him drive half-way across the country on some pie-eyed mission. Getting him mixed up with the police. Bringing disrepute to the church. Yes, he could quite understand it if Miles was mad at him.

With so many pressmen there, it was obvious that the story about the crazy pastor would be plastered all over the dailies. Some of the hacks were right there with them in the vestibule, hovering, their notebooks at the ready. When the sergeant left the room, they took their chance.

`Wilkerson – how do you spell that?'

`Where did you say you were from?'

`Why did you come here today?'

`How long have you been involved with the Dragons?'

David did his best to answer their questions although his mind was still spinning with his own concerns. How could God have let him down like this? He thought he'd found out God's will, but it had all gone terribly wrong. He was so sure that he was following God's prompting – why had things turned out this way?

*   *   *   *   *   *

It had all begun during one of David's late-night prayer sessions in his study. He had given up watching television and instead he now devoted two hours every night to prayer. It had been tough to begin with to spend such a long period in prayer, but he had persevered and now this special time was a joy for him.

He'd discovered that prayer wasn't just a matter of presenting God with a shopping list of things that you wanted Him to do. Of course he could ask God for things, but he could also praise Him and thank Him for all that He had done. And it was exciting to read the Bible through, section by section – not just the well-known bits, but all of it.

Yes, usually his two hours in prayer were a rich and exciting time for him.

But not tonight. He didn't know why, but tonight he just couldn't seem to settle. Maybe it was because he was alone in the house; the other members of the family were away visiting the children's grandparents in Pittsburg.

It wasn't as if God wasn't there with him. On the contrary, God seemed very near, but suddenly David felt an underlying sadness sweep over him, a terrible sadness that wouldn't go away. It filled the whole of his being, leaving room for nothing else.

`This must mean something, Lord. Tell me what it means,' he prayed. But still he was no clearer about the mysterious feeling.

He paced the floor, trying to understand what was going on, unable to settle. From the corner of his eye he caught sight of a copy of *Life* magazine. He picked it up, then hurriedly put it down again, his conscience bothering him.

How could he do such a thing? He was supposed to be praying. He wasn't going to let himself be interrupted by a crummy magazine. No, if God had something to tell him the answer wouldn't be there.

But he couldn't forget that magazine no matter what he did. Eventually he gave in. He settled down in his reading chair with palpitations in his chest and a sick, nervous feeling in the pit of his stomach. Why was he feeling like this? After all, it was only a magazine.

He turned the pages and there they were, staring out at him. Seven young boys, teenagers every one of them, who were on a murder charge in New York. They were accused of murdering a boy their own age, Michael Farmer, a polio victim.

According to the article it had been a brutal murder involving needless violence far beyond David's comprehension. The boys had attacked their defenceless victim in a park, stabbing him in the back seven times each, and then using their garrison belts to beat him about the head.

David felt desperately sorry for the murdered youngster. What a terrible way to die! He thanked God that violence like that didn't happen in his little town.

But what really got to him were those faces, the faces of the seven boys looking out at him from a simple pen-and-ink drawing. Looking out with hatred and defiance and despair and terror. Looking out for help that would never come.

And suddenly he knew. He must go to New York. Yes, he must go to New York and help those seven boys. They needed help so badly. And God was sending him to bring them help, to bring them hope.

The idea had no sooner passed through his head than he was already pooh-poohing it. How ridiculous! How could he help boys like that? He was a country preacher in a small town hundreds of miles away. He knew nothing about New York, nothing about the sort of lives that these boys lived and the problems that they experienced. How could he even begin to help them?

*   *   *   *   *   *

In the courtroom vestibule, detained by the police, David wondered whether he should have listened to the voice of reason that troubled night. At least he wouldn't have got into this mess – in a strange place, far away from home, under arrest. A disgrace to himself and to others. A disgrace to the God he loved so dearly.

The sergeant had returned and was unlocking the handcuffs.

`Okay, mister, you can go.'

David flexed his wrists, unable to believe that they were releasing him at last.

`Judge Davidson don't want no fuss, so he won't be pressing charges – not now. But you take care – he don't ever want to see you in this court again. You show your face once more and he'll throw the book at you.'

· `I'll make sure I stay away,' said David. `I'm not enjoying this any more than you are.'

`And I'll make double sure he keeps out of trouble,' added Miles.

They were free now. Free to go home. Back to Gwen and the children and the church. David sighed. Those poor dear people in his congregation. Whatever was he going to say to them? Not only had he been the cause of this awful fiasco – he had even got them to finance it.

*   *   *   *   *   *

The day after David saw the picture in *Life* magazine, his church held its regular Wednesday prayer meeting. It was bitter, wintry weather, so it wasn't surprising that only a couple of dozen church members had battled through the snow to be there.

David had shared his vision with them that Wednesday night. He'd showed them the picture in *Life* and told them about his God-given mission to go to New York and help those boys. He'd watched with love as church members came forward with their offerings, the money that would take him to New York.

Seventy-five dollars. The next morning he and Miles set off for the 350-mile drive to New York.

*   *   *   *   *   *

And this was how it had all ended. In public humiliation at the courtroom. Now he and Miles were free to go home to Philipsburg, and he would have to face up to the consequences of his actions. He would apologize to his congregation and he only hoped they could find it in their hearts to forgive him. And he prayed to God that He'd be merciful and allow him to remain in the ministry.

But first the two churchmen had to get out of the court and escape from another barrage of media attention. The press corps was already there, lined up and ready to pounce. David instinctively hugged his Bible for protection.

`What's that you're hiding?' asked one pressman.

`My Bible.'

`Are you ashamed of it or something?'

`No.'

`Let's see it then, mister. Hold it up nice and high.'

A dozen flashbulbs popped in unison. He should have known. Now his photograph would be plastered across all the newspapers for all to see. A stupid, naive country parson making a fool of himself in the big city.

`Come on, Miles,' urged David, his voice full of weariness. `Let's go home.'

Eventually they broke away from the crowd, got out of the court building and found where they had parked their car. David climbed in and locked the door. `I'm so sorry, Miles. I've been such a fool. I've let you down, I've let the church down, I've let God down. I'm so very, very sorry.'

Miles looked embarrassed and tried to offer his pastor a consoling hand. But the skinny preacher was already weeping, beyond any help that Miles could give him. He wept first for himself, out of shame and frustration. And then he remembered the desperate faces of those seven boys, no longer just a line drawing but now flesh and blood. And he wept again.

CHAPTER TWO

Good out of evil

'I just don't understand it, God,' said David, as he surveyed his parish from his favourite vantage point, an abandoned strip mine on a hill near the church. That was where he always went when he needed to sort something out in his mind. It seemed to him that he'd been spending a lot of time there recently, ever since he got back from New York.

Escapism maybe? Perhaps there was an element of that. Life hadn't been too easy after his disgraceful escapade in the big city. There were some members of the community who still hadn't forgiven him for what he had done to Philipsburg. They felt that he had sullied the town's reputation and they weren't going to forgive him too easily.

Not that he was finding it easy to forgive himself. It wasn't just the town he had shamed; he had brought disgrace to the church as well. His father's words had brought home to him just how serious his actions had been. 'You realize you might lose your ordination, David?' It had been a real possibility, one that David dreaded.

Mercifully, he seemed to have escaped that particular fate, but it wasn't surprising that some of David's fellow ministers were less than charitable towards him. How could they preach the gospel and be taken seriously when there was a lunatic pastor going around disturbing the processes of justice?

'Escapism? Yes, maybe I am trying to get away from it all', he said to himself. He broke off a blade of grass and idly picked at it. Another thought came to him. Jesus would have understood. Jesus went off into the wilderness to think and pray and be on his own. And he went off alone to the Garden of Gethsemane. That wasn't escapism.

Comforted by that thought, David's mood began to change. It hadn't all been a big disaster. His congregation had been very good to him in the circumstances. Of course, he hadn't felt very comfortable that first Sunday back in Philipsburg when he'd had to face them all in church. He felt a bit like a prisoner in the dock himself as he stood in the pulpit searching their faces in the hope of finding some glimmer of understanding.

How could he find the words to explain to them why he had interrupted the trial? To convince them that he really had believed he was following God's commands? To let them know that the last thing he wanted was to give the church a bad name? It had never been his intention to get his name in the papers and or to have people point him out in the street. His only thought had been to do God's will.

Now, facing his irate congregation, he was glad he could hide behind the pulpit so that no one would see his knees knocking. His mouth felt dry and his voice didn't sound at all like it usually did. And even as he spoke, he realized how feeble his excuses must sound to his parishioners. All his strongly held convictions sounded inadequate in the cold light of day.

All he could do was trust in God and hope that his congregation would take pity on him, even if they didn't fully understand why he had gone off on such a crazy mission.

`Never mind, Reverend,' said one of his elderly parishioners as she shook hands with him on the way out of church. She kept a grip of his hand and pulled him gently out of earshot of others before saying to him confidentially `We'll still have you, even if nobody else will.'

She had intended her words to be reassuring, but David didn't feel he was getting much of a vote of confidence.

Now, up on the hill by the strip mine, he looked out onto the quiet orderly little community that he served, a community of hard working, simple farmers. New York seemed a million miles away.

He'd seen so many terrible things there. Poor people living in squalor in slum buildings, whole families crushed together in one room. Dirt and debris everywhere. Even children of seven or eight were steeped in a violent culture. And perhaps worst of all, he had seen teenagers shooting heroin into their veins, desperate for a fix, and almost fainting with relief the moment the white substance hit their bloodstream.

He thanked God that the children of Philipsburg could grow up happy, able to breathe clean air, able to laugh and play and enjoy this special time of innocence. He thanked God that people could walk the streets or visit the local drugstore without being knifed. He thanked God that here in this small town even the poorest of people had somewhere decent to live.

Life might be simple out here in the country – some city folks might even call it a backwater existence – but at least it was wholesome, and he knew that his congregation had generous hearts. They were hearts filled with love, not with hatred and fear.

The pastor sighed. He would be taxing their generosity again pretty soon. Tonight he would tell them that he had again experienced God's call to go back to New York and help the boys in the trial. Once again he would ask them for money for the journey. How would they respond this time?

Some people would think he was mad, no doubt. Hadn't he learned to let well alone? As if he hadn't done enough damage! As if he hadn't made a big enough fool of himself already!

Yet he knew this was what he had to do. No matter how much he reasoned with himself, arguing the pros and cons, still the feeling wouldn't go away. It was an inner prompting, like the one he had felt the night he saw the article about the Farmer trial. He was sure it was the voice of God, even though obeying it had got him into trouble. And now God was telling him to go to New York a second time.

There was no human logic to it. He was in no better position this time to do anything than he had been originally. He knew nothing about New York, nothing about the life those kids lived. He couldn't even find his way around the tough neighbourhoods where they hung out. And because of his outburst at the Farmer trial, people would now regard him as a foolish crank. No, if anything, he was in an even worse position to go to New York.

He glanced at his watch and came back to reality. One o'clock. Gwen would have lunch ready. He'd better get back home or she'd be worried. She knew where he was, but she'd been kind of concerned about him ever since he got back from the trial.

The car door squeaked as he opened it. It sounded louder than usual.

'Yes, God,' he whispered. 'It may well be a crazy idea to go back and help those boys. But I can't get it out of my mind. If only I knew what I should do, what You really want me to do!'

He slammed the car door shut and started up the engine. The purring noise that it made was soothing. So ordinary. He released the hand-brake and set off, glad to feel the car move under his control.

`You don't need to be in control, David.' His mother's words rang through his head. He'd gone to see her on the way back from New York, hoping for some comfort and understanding. What he'd got from her were some very wise words.

`It's not you that's in control, David,' she'd said to him. `It's God. And if you can't understand why things have gone wrong, then remember this – God moves in a mysterious way sometimes. But you can bet your life he knows what He's doing.'

David smiled and changed up a gear. Maybe following God's will wasn't so hard after all.

* * * * * *

The following morning, David was in his car once again, on his way to New York with Miles. It was a rerun of their original journey. They didn't know what they were going to do when they got to the city – only that they were going to help the boys on trial.

First they headed for Broadway where David

decided they should stop the car. He wanted to get out and walk about for a while. Why? He didn't know. He just felt an urge to do it.

Half-way down the street, David heard someone calling his name. `Davie, hey, Davie.'

Was someone speaking to him? Surely not. He didn't know anyone in this neighbourhood. It must be another Davie. He kept on walking.

The voice called out again. `Davie. Preacher, come here.'

This time there was no mistaking who the voice was addressing. David swung round and saw a group of teenagers hanging about on the street, smoking cigarettes. They wore narrow trousers and zip-up jerkins. One of them was heading towards David, a big smile on his face.

`How did you know my name?' asked David.

`I saw your picture in the paper. You're famous, man. You're the one they threw out of the Farmer trial.'

The other boys leapt down from their perch on the wall and gathered round.

`Are you the one the cops had it in for? Tell us about it.'

`There's not much to tell,' said David. `I came here from the country because I'd read about the boys in the trial and I wanted to help them – not that I managed to do them much good.'

`Are you kidding?' said one of the boys. `You're a hero, man. Those cops messed you up good and proper. They treated you bad, just like they treat us.'

Suddenly, everything clicked. David caught a glimpse of God's mysterious plan. That fiasco in the courtroom had been necessary after all. How else could he have been accepted by boys like this? He was worlds apart from them, but now they had something in common – the cops had a downer on them both.

The boys who were from a gang called the Rebels invited David to come and meet a neighbouring gang of theirs called the GGIs. Apparently the initials stood for Grand Gangsters Incorporated.

David's encounter with the GGIs in their hide-out on 134th Street was a new and disturbing experience for him.

'Let's have some light in this place,' said David's guide, flicking a switch. When his eyes had adjusted to the light enough for him to see clearly, David was appalled at how filthy the basement was, and littered with vodka bottles.

Around the cold and dismal room, couples were having sex. But what upset him most was one of the gang girls named Maria. She was only thirteen or fourteen, but she held a can of beer in one hand and a cigarette in the other. And her dishevelled clothing clearly revealed that she had been indulging in sex play as well, even though she was very young.

Drink, sex and cigarettes. Not much to bring

joy to young lives, thought David. But there was worse to come. When David tried to explain to the youngsters that God could offer them a better life than this, Maria stopped him in his tracks.

`Save your breath, Preacher. It ain't no use. You ain't never gonna help me. Not while I'm doing this.'

Maria rolled up her sleeve and showed David the inside of her elbow. It was covered in tiny bite-like marks. David assumed they were needle marks, the sign of a heroin addict.

The girl looked at David with a hopeless expression in her eyes. `I'm a mainliner, Preacher. There ain't anybody who can help me. Not you, not anybody.'

Surely this wasn't the case! David felt a terrible gnawing in the pit of his stomach. He desperately wanted to contradict her, to tell her that there was some hope for her, that she wasn't doomed to a ghastly premature death. But what did he know about such things?

He looked around at her friends to see how they reacted to what she'd said. They were stony faced. They knew Maria was right. The preacher might be naive enough to think that heroin addicts could get over their addiction. But they knew better. They'd seen plenty of kids like Maria go to an early grave. There was no hope – not for mainliners like her.

Still reeling from this discovery, David thanked his hosts and headed back for the car.

Miles had been getting worried – David had been gone a long time.

`Where on earth have you been? I imagined all sorts of terrible things happening to you.'

`They have, Miles, but not in the way you think. I'm all right. But as for those poor street kids – I had no idea just how much they needed help. And I've no idea how we're going to give it to them. But first there are some other kids we've got to do something about.'

He hadn't forgotten that the whole purpose of their visit was to help the boys in the Farmer trial. And after the way God had helped him get along with the Rebels and the GGIs, he was convinced that everything would work out just fine. They headed for the DA's office with renewed confidence, determined to obtain permission to see the Farmer trial boys.

Their hopes were cruelly dashed. The district attorney was unyielding, no matter how much they argued for a chance to contact the boys.

`But we only want to help them . . .'

`That may well be, but it makes no difference. There's no way you're going to get permission to see those boys. It simply isn't allowed. Why, if you wanted to see them, you'd need each of the parents to give you written permission.'

That was it. David could begin to see a way ahead. If what he had to do was get the parents' permission, then that was what he'd do.

`I'd like the names and addresses of the boys. Can you provide me with them, please?'

`I'm sorry. I can't release that information. Not for you or for anybody.'

Outside the office, David looked at Miles and sighed. Every time they had a glimmer of hope, they had yet another setback. The DA wasn't going to make things easier for them, that was for sure. So how on earth were they going to find the parents of the boys. They didn't even know the boys' names.

David put his hand in his pocket. It was there – the article from *Life* magazine that had started the whole thing off. Maybe that would give them some clues?

It did. It contained the name of the gang leader, Luis Alvarez.

`I'm going to find that boy's folks if I have to ring up every Alvarez in New York,' declared David. `You'd better stay in the car, Miles. You could be in for a long wait.'

Armed with a pile of dimes, David headed for a telephone. His face fell when he saw just how many entries for Alvarez there were in the telephone book – in Manhattan alone there were more than two hundred.

The response he got was not encouraging. Ordinary, decent folk don't like strangers ringing them up and asking whether their son is on trial for murder. Sometimes the question

would be met with a stunned silence. Or someone would shout at him angrily and slam down
the receiver. After about forty phone calls, David
could see that he was engaged in a futile task.
He stuffed the remaining dimes into his pocket
and tramped back to the car.

David and Miles were now in despair. They
had to find the boys' parents. That was their
only hope. But it seemed an impossible task.
There was no way they were going to solve this
problem themselves.

There was only one answer. They'd have to
rely on God to guide them. Together in the car,
the two men bowed their head and prayed.

`Lord, if there's something You want us to do,
we can only do it with Your guidance. We don't
know what to do or where to go. Show us the
way, Lord.'

They started up the car and headed north, the
direction that the car was facing. Then they got
lost on the circular road in Central Park and
when they eventually found an exit they ended
up in Spanish Harlem.

`I think we should stop here,' said David. He
felt again an urge to stop the car, just as he had
done earlier when he met the Rebels gang.

They found a spot to park, and David walked
a short distance along the street. He didn't
understand why, but it felt right to be there
somehow. He caught sight of a group of boys
who were sitting by the roadside.

`I'm looking for a boy named Luis Alvarez,' said David. `Do you know where he lives?'

No reply came from the boys – not even any sign of acknowledgment. David shrugged and walked on farther. But he was being followed. By a small Negro boy.

`You want Luis Alvarez? The one that killed the cripple?'

`That's right,' said David. `Do you know where he lives?'

`I sure do,' said the boy. `He lives right there.'

He pointed to a tenement block. It was right beside David's car.

David came out in a cold sweat. It was uncanny. Somehow he had managed to park right in front of the Alvarez house. He uttered a silent prayer of thanks and headed for the Alvarez apartment.

When he reached the third floor where the Alvarez family lived, the dingy brown hallway reeked of stale urine and neglect, but the family's name was neatly painted on the door.

`Excuse me,' he shouted. `I'm looking for Mr Alvarez.' He didn't understand the reply he got in Spanish, but he cautiously pushed open the door and ventured in.

The man was dark-skinned and he held a rosary in his hands. When he saw David, he beamed.

`You are the preacher,' he said. `Davie. From the courtroom.'

Mr Alvarez rose to his feet and held out his hand.

`I've been waiting for you. I've been praying you come and help my Luis.'

The father's prayers had been answered. And David's too. He explained how he needed signed permission in order to see the boy and Mr Alvarez wrote it for him in his painstakingly slow handwriting.

`I need the names and addresses of the other parents too,' said David. `Do you happen to have them?'

`No,' said Mr Alvarez. `I no have contact with Luis's friends. They're bad boys. You trust in God – he'll help you find them.'

David made his way back down the stairs, admiring Mr Alvarez's faith. He felt very sorry for him. How must it feel to have a son on a horrific murder charge? David tried to imagine how he would feel if it were his own child that was on trial. The very idea was unbearable.

He was still deep in thought when he stepped into the street, only to collide with a lad of seventeen who was on his way upstairs at full speed. The boy paused and looked quizzically at the stranger's face.

`Say, aren't you the preacher guy from Luis's trial? The one the cops threw out? I'm Angelo. Angelo Morales. I'm a member of Luis's gang.'

It was another happy meeting. Angelo

Morales knew where all the other defendants lived and was glad to guide the two men around the city to the homes of the various boys.

`Why weren't you there with the gang? The night that Michael Farmer was murdered?' asked David.

`I should have been,' said Angelo. `But I had toothache. And as far as we were concerned it was just an ordinary night.'

Just an ordinary night. That's what they had thought. The gang had gone out in search of trouble – `going on a rumble' they called it. It just so happened it was the disabled boy, Michael Farmer, who was in their path. If they hadn't met him, perhaps they'd have vented their frustrations in a spot of `jitterbugging' – fighting with rival gangs.

It was beyond David's comprehension that young people could go out deliberately looking for violence. Angelo seemed so ordinary. Just like any other kid. But the lives these youngsters lived were extraordinary, a far cry from those of teenagers back home in Philipsburg. What made boys like Angelo turn to gangs and fighting for their thrills?

Talking to Angelo, David began to understand some of the reasons. These New York boys suffered from a mixture of loneliness, boredom and anger. The gangs provided a sense of belonging that they often didn't get from their family or neighbours. And fighting helped to while away the hours that hung so heavily. Time passes slowly if you don't have a purpose.

And violence was an outlet for their anger too. They didn't know why they were angry. But they knew that life wasn't fair, and they seemed to have drawn the short straw.

Angelo lived up to his name – truly he was a messenger sent from God, albeit an unlikely one. The two men very quickly collected all the signatures they needed, and bade farewell to their young companion. God bless Angelo! David was sure He would. Hadn't He answered their prayers in wonderful, unexpected ways?

God had been faithful to them, and now they would be able to carry out His work. They'd be able to go and see the seven boys in prison.

When they returned to the district attorney's office, the DA was amazed to see them back so soon, especially when he found that they'd brought along the necessary documentation.

`Now will you let us see the boys?' requested David.

`I'll call the jail straight away. If the boys agree, you can go ahead and see them.'

The boys did agree. Very soon each of them signed a form to say they would talk with David. But another stumbling block lay in David's way, and this time it was the prison chaplain who caused the problem. Apparently he took the boys' forms and changed them so that they read `We will not talk with Reverend David Wilkerson.'

David was totally bewildered by the chaplain's action. `Why on earth would he do such a thing? The boys agreed to see us, didn't they?'

`The chaplain feels it might be disturbing for the boys to speak to you at this stage,' explained the DA. `Meeting someone new might unsettle them.'

`But they want to see me. How can he stop them?'

`I'm afraid the chaplain has made up his mind. I can't overrule his decision. I'm very sorry.'

Once again it appeared that David and Miles had been wasting their time. The authorities weren't going to budge an inch – there was no way they would see the Farmer trial boys. All that was left for them to do was to go back home to Pennsylvania.

`Well, Lord,' said David. `I was just beginning to think I understood Your mysterious ways. It seems that I was wrong. I'm completely stumped.'

Both David and Miles were bewildered by all that had happened during this second visit to New York. To get so close to seeing the boys, to obtain all the signatures against all the odds, then be stopped by the prison chaplain! Why should God lead them so far then close the door so firmly against them?

`God certainly acts in a mysterious way,' confessed David as they drove back home.

`He sure does,' said Miles, with a yawn. It had been a long and tiring day.

Then suddenly, unexpectedly, David's eyes lit up with excitement.

`I don't understand what God is planning, Miles. I don't understand it at all.' A smile came over David's lips. `But I know a man who might.'

_____

CHAPTER THREE

A greater purpose

`Hello, Grandpap', said David. `I need to speak to you. Can I come over?'

`You sure can,' replied David's grandfather. `I'll be waiting.'

So David was back in the car for a lengthy drive to his grandfather's farm near Toledo, Ohio.

Grandpap was retired now, seventy-nine years old, but for most of his life he had been a preacher. His father and grandfather had been preachers too, and his son, David's father, was following the family tradition. But Grandpap had been no ordinary preacher.

David chuckled to himself as he remembered the time when his father had invited Grandpap to preach at his church. The event didn't turn out quite as expected.

`I want all those people out here to hear you loud and clear,' Grandpap told the congregation. `They're going to know that this church is alive.'

A few eyebrows were raised, but everyone did as Grandpap ordered. David's father wondered what the congregation would make of it all. But his biggest worry was what would Grandpap do next. He knew what he was like.

`You deacons – get 'those windows open,'
continued Grandpap. `The rest of you, on your
feet. You're going to do some marching. Hup,
two, hup, two, hup, two . . . That's right. Now
clap your hands in time to the music.'

It was a bizarre sight, the entire congregation
marching round the church and clapping their
hands. The drill continued for a quarter of an
hour, and only then did Grandpap let the
congregation sing – but they still had to clap and
march as well! Every so often, Grandpap would
go over and open the window a little wider so
that the neighbours could hear what was going
on.

David's father was terribly embarrassed to see
his congregation being treated in such an
unorthodox way. All this marching and clapping
and loud singing was a far cry from the sedate
sort of service normally held on a Sunday
evening. But eventually he overcame his
reservations and joined in one of the songs with
gusto.

As it turned out, the pastor needn't have
worried about his father's visit. Grandpap had
certainly made an impression on the locals, but
it was a good one.

`That sure was a fine service you had last
night,' said one of the neighbours the next day.
`Why the whole neighbourhood's buzzing with
talk about it! We haven't heard singing like that
in here for a very long time.'

But Grandpap wasn't only unconventional. He was a deeply spiritual man as well. He knew the power of God and he believed that because of Pentecost, the time when God sent his Holy Spirit down upon the Apostles, God's power was at work in the Church. And if God was powerful, you had to take risks, to pray for something specific, to pray as if you believed God would listen to your prayer. That was the most important thing that David learned from his grandpap.

David remembered the day when, as a small boy, he had put that to the test by praying for his father's life. David's father had been very ill, so ill, in fact, that the doctors had given him only a couple of hours to live. His agonized screams were so loud that David could hear them on his way home from school.

The boy was desperate to go and join his father, but his mother wouldn't let him. She slammed the bedroom door shut – not quickly enough – though, because David had already seen his father's blood stained sickbed. He knew there was something terribly wrong with him.

It suddenly occurred to him that his father might die. How could he! It was unthinkable! His brain felt numb. Then Grandpap's words echoed through his head. `Be specific in your prayers, David. That's what you must do if you want your prayers to be powerful.'

David took Grandpap at his word. To be

honest, he couldn't really see how his feeble prayers could help someone in such a desperate state as his father. But he trusted his grandpap, so he did as he'd been told. He went to the basement of the house, knelt down, and prayed – not timidly, but as loud as he possibly could.

He didn't realize it, but all the time he was praying, his voice was ringing round and round the house, amplified by the hot air pipes. It was as if he were speaking through a loudspeaker. Everyone could hear his prayer, including his sick father.

Father was deeply moved. `Let me see David,' he asked. David was duly sent for and brought to his father's bedside.

`Come here, son,' whispered Mr Wilkerson to the twelve-year-old. `I've got something important to say to you.'

He turned to his wife. `Open the Bible, honey,' he said. `Matthew twenty-one, twenty-two.'

David's mother read the verse out loud. `And all things whatsoever ye shall ask in prayer, believing, ye shall receive.'

`Do you believe that?' asked his father.

`I do,' said David. `I believe that Jesus can make you better, Daddy.'

He sounded confident, but really he was as surprised as anyone when Dr Brown came back into the room and announced that Dad was getting better. And he was. He was getting stronger every moment. It was a real miracle!

Yes, looking back at his childhood, David realized that Dad's illness and Grandpap's faith had expanded his vision of what God could do. He only hoped his Grandpap could work another miracle for him right now.

Try as he might, David couldn't work out how to help the boys in the Farmer trial. He was too full of concerns and anxieties to see a way forward. But Grandpap, wise old Grandpap, would know what to do.

David's car drew up at Grandpap's farm. He was glad to be back in this familiar place where everything seemed safe and right. Glad that he wasn't on his own. He got out of the car and shut the door. Grandpap was standing in the yard waiting for him.

`Now then, my boy,' said Grandpap. `Tell me what's on your mind.'

David poured out his tale from the very beginning, ending with all his hopes and uncertainties. Would he be able to help the Farmer trial boys? How could he tell whether that was what God wanted of him?

The answer that Grandpap gave was not what David had expected. `No, David, I don't think you've a call to help the boys in that trial,' said the old man. `If that was what the Lord wanted, I don't think He would have stopped you at every turn.'

David was disappointed. He'd been hoping that Grandpap of all people would understand how he felt. Nobody seemed to appreciate how much he cared about those boys.

Grandpap saw the disappointment in David's eyes, and continued. `God's got work for you to do all right. I'm quite sure about that. But it isn't only with those seven boys.'

David blinked. He couldn't see what Grandpap was getting at.

`Don't you understand, David? The Lord wants you to help all the boys in New York who're scared and lonely and mixed up. It's not just those gang boys who need you. You've got to think big.'

* * * * * *

New York beckoned again, and this time David approached the city with a new openness. Yes, he'd do whatever he could to help the Farmer trial boys. He wasn't going to give up on them so easily. But now he was open to new possibilities as well. There was a mission for him on those New York streets, he was sure of that. If only he could work out what it was!

But first he was to see one of the boys who had been released from jail. Four of the boys had been imprisoned, including the leader, Luis. One of the others was preparing to flee the country with his parents and another was to receive treatment in a mental hospital. The final boy was being sent home. David decided to pay his parents a visit.

The boy's mother ushered David into the cramped kitchen with its lingering smell of Spanish food. Normally David liked Spanish food, but today it made him feel sick. He turned to the anxious-looking woman.

`What are you going to do when your son comes home?' he asked. `Will you be taking him away from here?'

`I wish we could,' replied the boy's mother. `You should see the things that people write about us on our walls, terrible things. They hate us, but what can we do? How could we move away? My husband has a job here.'

`Why don't I look after your boy?' offered David. `He'd be safe with my family in Pennsylvania.'

`You're very kind,' said the woman. `But he has a family of his own. We'll send him away to stay with some of his own relations. He won't be here for long, I can guarantee that.'

She slowly rose to her feet and sighed. `Soon he'll be far away from here. It will be as if he had never lived.' She looked pale and gaunt, as if the soul had gone out of her.

As he made his way back out, David couldn't help noticing piles of newspapers. They were all over the apartment, piled to the ceiling. He caught sight of some headlines and realized that they contained stories about the trial.

Suddenly he understood what the mother was going through. How awful it must be to read about a murder and know that your son was to blame! To know that your own flesh and blood was responsible for the death of another young man!

David thanked God he'd never had to face that kind of pain. Being ostracized by a few people in Pennsylvania was nothing compared with the hatred and recrimination this poor woman had to face every day of her life.

*   *   *   *   *   *

Back in Pennsylvania, David reflected on his trip to New York. Grandpap had been right. One by one, doors had been shut to keep him away from the boys in the Farmer trial. Helping them definitely wasn't going to be his mission. So what was? He still felt a calling to New York, a need to be there in and amongst the squalor and the filth and the hopelessness.

Over the next few months David set aside some time to explore New York and find out what was really needed in the city. Between March and June of that year he spent his one day off a week making the long return trip to New York. The city was calling him – but to what?

It was at this time that little things people had said to him suddenly took on a new significance. One of the drug addicts he'd met, Maria, had mentioned that the Bedford-Stuyvesant part of Brooklyn was the very worst area of the city. David later discovered that it had more murders per square foot than anywhere else in the world.

He decided he would have to go there. This was the New York of the Farmer trial boys and other boys like them. This was the New York where young people were living desperate lives, where they were lucky if they lived to see adulthood. Life was cheap in New York, especially in Bedford-Stuyvesant. David felt he needed to see the locality for himself, although he knew it would be an unsavoury and unsettling experience.

On his first excursion into the neighbourhood the already grim area appeared even more dismal because of the cold weather. It was winter, and the snowploughs had been trying to clear the streets. David had to battle his way through slush and the grey mounds of snow they'd left behind. He squelched and slid his way through the streets, feeling a very long way from the security of Pennsylvania.

Back in Philipsburg, people knew one another and looked after those in need, but here it seemed as if nobody cared. He had seen a drunk lying helplessly on the pavement in the cold and wet, but when David reported it to a policeman, he didn't do anything to help. The poor man could have died of hypothermia.

There was dirty garbage everywhere and most things seemed to be broken. In such a harsh and inhospitable environment, it was no wonder that people found it hard to live decent lives.

David had finished looking round and was just about to return to his car when he was startled by three loud noises. They sounded like gunshots. For a moment, he froze with fear. Something terrible must be happening.

He pulled himself together with difficulty and looked to see how his fellow passers-by were reacting. To his amazement, they were just going about their everyday business, apparently unconcerned about the noises which he had found so alarming. He was beginning to wonder whether he had imagined the sound of the gunshots.

But he hadn't. A few minutes later a police car sped to the scene and the officers emerged from a boarding house with a man who had blood dripping from a wound in his shoulder. An incident like this would have caused a sensation in Philipsburg, but here people didn't bat an eyelid. To them violence was something they lived with all the time.

It was with some trepidation that David settled down to spend the night in his car. He could only just afford his petrol – there was no way he could pay for a hotel room as well. He pulled a blanket over himself and tried his best to keep warm.

The familiar and comforting streets of Pennsylvania seemed a million miles away, streets where people could walk in safety and innocent children could happily play. Part of him wished he was back in Philipsburg with Gwen and the children.

But another part, deep down, knew that God had something for him to do. He searched for God's purpose in his sleep just as he did in his waking hours, but nothing was clear to him. He tossed and turned in his chilly car, praying that tomorrow would bring an answer to his questions.

*   *   *   *   *   *

Only as the weeks and months passed and David's weekly visits multiplied did he realize how foolish he'd been to sleep in the car. He'd put himself in a lot of danger and he discovered it wasn't the adults he needed to fear the most. Strangely enough, it was the eight-to-ten-year-olds, the `Little People' as they were called, who were most likely to have attacked him. They'd have killed him for no reason at all.

Violence was what these children saw round about them, and a life of violence was all they had to look forward to. They would spend their teenage years as members of gangs and these weren't like the gangs back home whose members hung around talking about cars and sport.

No, the teen gangs in Brooklyn filled their time with alcohol and hard core porn, and acted

out what they'd seen on paper in real life sex
gatherings. Or they'd go out on a `rumble' as
they called it, looking for a fight with another
gang. These gang rumbles were not just harmless
horseplay, but desperate fights in which young
people could be maimed or even killed.

The lives of these young people reached
depths of depravity that David had never before
encountered in his life and ministry so far. He
found it extremely difficult to see young people
throwing away their lives in this way, living
without hope, knowing only hatred and fear.

But the worst thing of all, he felt, was the drug
abuse. The youngsters saw drugs as a way to
escape from their hopeless existence and gain
some pleasure, even if it was only fleeting. Drugs
were a constant temptation to them as drug
dealers even hung around the schools trying to
get young children hooked on marijuana. From
that they would often progress to a more deadly
substance, heroin. And once they fell under its
spell, their fate was sealed.

On one of his visits to New York, David heard
terrible screams coming from one of the
buildings. The person making all the noise was a
young man, and he was obviously in agony.

David asked one of the man's neighbours
what was wrong. She explained to him that the
man was a twenty-year-old drug addict.

`It ain't no use trying to help him,' said the
woman. `He needs a fix and he ain't got no stuff.

He'll be like that till he can get his hands on some more,'.

`But we must be able to do something,' insisted David. `Surely there's somewhere we can take him – a hospital perhaps?'

`You must be kidding, mister. None of the hospitals round here have room for a kid like that. There ain't nobody that can help him, you can bet your life on that.'

She was right. At that time there was only one place in New York where drug addicts could go for help – Riverside Hospital – and there was no way the hospital could even begin to cope with the number of addicts there were in the city. The only other establishment with a drug-abuse programme open to New York youngsters was in Lexington, Kentucky.

David was forced to face the facts. For the poor kids in New York, there was no escape from their misery. It seemed there was nothing to give them hope.

`I'll tell you what I don't understand,' said David to Angelo, who was showing him around the city. `What is it that makes these kids lead such desperate lives? Why do they need the alcohol and the sex and the drugs and the violence?'

`It's simple,'said Angelo. `It helps them to forget'.

`But what is it they need to forget?' prompted David.

`That they're lonesome,' said his young friend. `That's all, Preacher. They need to forget that they're lonesome.'

It was beginning to make sense. That was the real problem behind all the others. These kids needed to know that they mattered, that they were important to somebody, even if the only people who cared about them were their fellow gang members. Unless they could believe that somebody loved them, all the drug abuse programmes, all the education, all the preaching in the world would make no difference.

David was beginning to see how big his task really was. What these young people needed was a fresh start in a loving environment. Somewhere they would feel secure, where they would have a comfortable bed to sleep in, warm clothes to wear and plenty of understanding. But how could he provide that? There were so many kids in desperate need!

David sighed. It was a hopeless task. After all, he hadn't even been able to help the seven boys in the Farmer trial. His efforts were just a drop in the ocean.

A police siren blared in the distance. More trouble. `God help the victim – and the offender,' prayed David silently.

Suddenly he felt better. He knew that his prayer would be answered. God would help the people of New York – hadn't he already called David from his safe haven in Pennsylvania onto the dark streets of New York? David was only just beginning to understand why.

It was a big task that lay before him. At times he felt it was impossible. But David remained quietly confident. The job might be too big for David's human efforts, but nothing was too big for God. David would just have to wait and the Lord's plan would unfold – in His own good time.

* * * * * *

By the time another week had passed and David was preparing for another day off in New York, his mood had changed somewhat. He still had high hopes for the boys of New York, but the more he thought about it, the bigger the task seemed, and the less well-equipped he appeared to be to deal with it.

How could he succeed where so many teachers, welfare workers and police officers had failed? After all, he was only a skinny preacher from Pennsylvania, wandering the streets on his day off. He knew very little about crime or violence or drug abuse. He had no money. He had no support from any organization – only from Gwen, his wife, waiting patiently for him back home.

But maybe that was just as well. It would teach him to rely on God rather than on his own strength or position. `Not by might, nor by power, but by My Spirit, saith the Lord of Hosts.'

If these boys were going to make a fresh start, it would be the Holy Spirit that would make it happen, not David Wilkerson.

But now David could feel the Spirit's prompting yet again. Up till now, David's role had been that of an observer, getting to know the city and the boys. He had watched how they lived and listened to some of them. But now he knew he would have to get involved in their lives in a new way. He would have to go and speak to them.

The thought filled him with fear. What would he say? How would they react to him? Would he be a laughing stock? Or would someone listen? There was only one thing to do. Go ahead and try it and see what happened.

Never in his wildest dreams could he have imagined what the consequences would be.

CHAPTER FOUR

Street preaching

David was determined to speak to the toughest of the New York gangs, so he asked around to find out who they were. It emerged that the two most notorious gangs both belonged to the Fort Greene area of Brooklyn. Fort Greene was a massive estate housing more than thirty thousand people, mainly from the black and Puerto Rican sections of the population. Many of the people there had no jobs and depended on welfare payments.

The Mau Maus were a gang of young Puerto Ricans who had a reputation for horrendous violence. In their street fights, they used an awesome array of weapons – guns, chains, baseball bats and switchblades (flick knives) – to strike fear into the heart of their enemies.

The Chaplains were a black gang who were also based in Fort Greene. Although there was fierce rivalry between gangs in different areas of the city, the Mau Maus and the Chaplains belonged to the same `turf'. They devoted their energy to fighting enemy gangs and the police, but they didn't fight against each other.

The Mau Maus were instantly recognizable because of their uniform, which was a red jacket with a double M on the back and a Tyrolean-style cap. Passers-by would quickly step aside to make way for them and made sure they didn't do anything which could be interpreted as a threat.

These boys weren't reasonable. They'd kill you as soon as look at you, just for being there. Everyone had heard about the awful things that happened to ordinary folk who just happened to cross paths with the Mau Maus.

There was the candy store lady, for example. The Mau Maus robbed her store one day. The poor woman was scared out of her mind. The boys looked as if they meant business. She learned her lesson the hard way. When she tried to call the police, they stabbed her in the stomach with a butcher's knife.

The Chaplains, Fort Greene's black gang, were just as violent and were feared throughout the whole city. Both gangs were full of hard young men who would kill you as soon as look at you. They were used to getting their own way through intimidation or violence.

How would they react to a skinny preacher from the country who came to them with a message of love? David knew it wouldn't be easy to speak to them, but he relied on the power of the Holy Spirit to work on them rather than his own strength.

He had, however, decided to take along a friend of his for moral support, a trumpet player named Jimmy Stahl. The two men set off at the crack of dawn and headed for Fort Greene. They decided upon a spot near a lamp-post in Edward Street, not far from the subway station. Parking near the local school, they nervously prepared to speak to their audience.

The plan was for Jimmy to attract a crowd by playing his trumpet, then when enough people had gathered, David would preach to them. Jimmy started to play `Onward Christian Soldiers' as loudly and brightly as he could. Surely people would take notice?

They did. People flung their windows open and leaned out to see where the music was coming from. Little children ran out from tenement blocks and gathered in a circle round the musician. `It's a circus, it's a circus,' they cried. The little gathering was obviously the highlight of their day.

Jimmy kept playing, repeating the hymn over and over again till he was beginning to be sick of it. He'd played it more than a dozen times by now. No one was complaining though.

Jimmy lifted an eyebrow and looked at David to find out what to do now. Maybe it was time for a different tune?

`Don't stop,' said David. `The teenagers are starting to come over now.'

The children were quickly joined by older boys and girls, including some who were dressed in a similar style. David assumed they were the members of the gangs that he'd heard so much about. The Chaplains were the first to arrive. It wasn't often you heard music in these dreary streets.

They were about to be joined by the Mau Maus when suddenly a police car screeched to a halt right beside the assembled crowd. By now there were nearly a hundred people gathered round the two churchmen.

Two burly police officers got out and jostled their way to where David and Jimmy were standing. David was surprised at how rough they were with the bystanders, poking them in the ribs with their batons. `Beat it. I want you off this patch before I can count ten,' said one of the officers. The policemen back in Philipsburg didn't treat people like that. David swallowed and tried to look respectable.

`Listen,' said the officer. `You'd better move yourselves. I don't want no riot on my hands. These kids can act real crazy at times.'

`We were only preaching,' protested David, lamely.

`Well, you got no right,' said the officer. `I don't care what it is you're doing – you ain't doing it here.'

`Just a minute,' said David, angry at the high-handed way the officers were behaving. `Surely any American citizen can address the public like this.'

`Only if they speak under an American flag,'

replied the officer. `You two don't appear to have a flag with you.'

`That's no problem, Officer,' said David. `We'll get one.'

Without another word, David turned and walked briskly away.

The two police officers gave each other a knowing smile. These cranks were always trying out new scams, but they soon gave up if you handled them right.

They were just about to clear the crowd when David emerged from a nearby school, carrying a piano-stool in one hand and an enormous American flag in the other. He propped up the flag and looked hopefully at the police.

`Now are you satisfied, Officer?'

The belligerent policeman shrugged his shoulders and reluctantly the cops got back into their patrol car.

The crowd clapped their hands enthusiastically and whistled their appreciation. They didn't know who these guys were, but they were heroes. The police had no right to poke their nose in where they weren't wanted, and it was good that the skinny man had sent them packing.

Jimmy started to play `Onward, Christian Soldiers' once again, and the music attracted yet more people to join the throng. Eventually David decided that the crowd was big enough and signalled to Jimmy to stop. As the last note of the chorus died away, David climbed onto the piano-stool, cleared his throat and began to speak to the crowd.

`Ladies and gentlemen,' he began. `I've come a long way to speak to you today – three hundred miles from my church in Pennsylvania.'

His words were lost in the wind and the general din. Everyone had turned their attention to a young couple who were doing a sexy dance in front of the preacher. The crowd was egging them on, enjoying this unexpected floor show, and the atmosphere had turned sour. He thought he'd got their sympathy, but now the moment had passed, and nobody seemed to want to listen.

After he'd tried for a few minutes to get the crowd to quieten down, David gave up and simply bowed his head in prayer. He looked rather odd, standing on the stool in silence, but he didn't worry about what people thought of him. All he wanted was for people to hear what the Lord had to say to them.

`Lord, if you want me to speak to these people, you're going to have to make them listen,' he prayed. I can't do it on my own.'

His reverent attitude was infectious. Silence spread throughout the crowd and they waited expectantly to hear what the skinny man had to say.

David began to speak, still very much afraid, but trusting in the Holy Spirit to give him the right words to say. The preacher had chosen as his text John 3:16, `For God so loved the world that He gave His only begotten son that whosoever believeth in Him should not perish, but have everlasting life.'

`You may not feel that God loves you,' began David, `but He does, and that's why I'm here today. I know that you may not think of yourself as religious people, and God knows that too.'

It didn't matter how many terrible things they'd done or how far away from God they seemed, explained David. God could forgive even murderers.

`You might look tough and hard and cruel on the outside, but God can see what's inside you. God knows your past and how bad you've been, but He also knows how good your future could be if you would only turn to Him.'

He looked at the crowd expectantly. They were still listening intently, but David wanted to take things further. What he wanted to see was commitment. But maybe that was asking too much from people he didn't know, people whose background was so alien to Christianity.

But wasn't that the heart of the gospel? `I came not to call the righteous, but sinners to repentance.'

`Do you believe in miracles?' asked David. `I'm going to ask God for a miracle. I'm going to ask him to change your life right now. To make each of you a new person in Christ.'

David closed his eyes and prayed for God to come upon the crowd and do His work, but when he opened his eyes nothing seemed to have changed.

`Come right on up to the front if you want to speak to me,' he urged, but nobody seemed to want to take him up on his offer. What was he to do now? He was standing in front of all these people and he had no idea what to do next.

Then suddenly he found himself stepping out in faith the way his Grandpap had always advised him, the way he had done when his father was at death's door.

`I know that some of you here are from the Mau Maus and the Chaplains, and you have a reputation for being pretty tough.' He hesitated, then put out a challenge to them. `If you're as tough as people say, you won't be scared to come and shake hands with a skinny preacher like me, will you?'

A frisson of excitement ran through the crowd, but nobody came forward. Then someone from the back of the crowd shouted out, `What's the matter with you, Buckboard? Are you scared?'

A big black boy slowly made his way to the front of the crowd, followed by three other black gang members. David grew more and more nervous. After all, these were dangerous young men, and he wasn't sure what they were going to do.

To his surprise the tall black man had a smile on his face and he shook hands with David quite amiably.

`I'm Buckboard,' said the boy. `I'm the President of the Chaplains. This is Stagecoach, and these are my two War Lords.'

David talked to them some more about how God wanted to give them new lives, then one of them asked `How do we get these new lives then?'

`You must kneel down and ask God to send the Holy Spirit into your lives so that you can be new creatures in Christ.'

He hadn't really believed that they would do it. It's one thing to kneel at the altar in church, but it's quite another to kneel in the middle of the street in front of so many people.

But to his surprise, all four of them did as they were told. David prayed for them, then the four gang members got up and went back to their places on the pavement. Now it was the turn of the Chaplains' rival gang, the Mau Maus. The crowd wasn't going to let them off the hook.

`Where's Nicky and Israel? You gonna let the Chaplains get one over on you? Show them you ain't scared.'

The Mau Mau leader sauntered to the front with a surly looking young man following on behind. The president said his name was Israel

57

and shook hands with David. He introduced his surly companion as Nicky, the gang's vice-president.

Nicky refused to take David's hand. He stood there awkwardly, a cigarette in his hand and a look of defiance on his face.

Then he looked David straight in the eye. `Go to hell, preacher,' he said in a peculiar strangulated voice.

David looked back at him unflinchingly. `I know you don't like me, Nicky, but I want you to know that I love you. I love you, and Jesus loves you too.'

`Just you come near me, Preacher,' said Nicky, `and I'll kill you. I swear I will.'

David had no doubt that he meant it. This was the hardest young man that he had ever met.

'How will God find a way to soften Nicky's heart?' he wondered.

*   *   *   *   *   *

Even though he had begun to make contact with larger numbers of boys from the roughest areas of New York, David still yearned to help the seven boys in the Farmer trial. Hearing that Luis was to be transferred to the Elmira prison in New York, he went to the station on the day of the transfer, hoping to get a chance to talk to him when the prisoners were taken off the train. But he didn't manage to see the boy.

However, he did meet someone else who

would turn out to be invaluable to him. One spring evening he heard a gospel song coming from a tenement block in Spanish Harlem. It appeared that there was some sort of church upstairs. Of course he had to go up and investigate for himself.

He knocked at the door and waited for a reply, not knowing what to expect. He hadn't bargained on such an enthusiastic reaction. The woman who answered the door let out a cry of excitement and spoke in Spanish to her friends. He didn't understand what she said but he gathered that she was very pleased to see him.

He found out that the congregation was part of the Spanish branch of the Assemblies of God and it met in the home of the Reverend Vincente Ortez, the group's pastor. They had seen David's picture in the Farmer trial reports and had been praying for him.

David was made to feel very welcome, and everyone was keen to hear how he had become involved in the trial. He told them the story from the beginning, and outlined his vision that God could help the street kids. They were so inspired by what he said that they invited him back the following day to speak at a meeting of ministers.

`Where are you staying?' asked the Reverend Ortez.

`In my car,' replied David. `I'm afraid I couldn't afford a hotel room anywhere.'

The Reverend Ortez was horrified. `Don't you

realize how dangerous that is? You must stay at our house whenever you are in New York.'

David was pleased to be able to spend the night indoors and the bunk bed he slept on was more welcome than any fancy hotel bed could have been. It was basic accommodation, but as David discovered, the couple lived as simply as they could and used the rest of their money for God's work.

When David arrived at the meeting which the Reverend Ortez had arranged, he was astonished to find he was speaking to people from sixty-five of the Spanish Assemblies of God. How had the reverend managed to get them all together at such short notice? David only hoped they wouldn't be disappointed in what he had to say.

He could only be honest with them and tell them why he'd become involved in New York and how uncertain he was about what he should be doing next. Whenever he tried to help the Farmer trial boys, God seemed to close every door in his face. He told them how he had preached at Fort Greene, but he didn't know whether he was meant to carry on and do something similar again.

The church representatives were ambitious in their plans. They decided to hold a mass rally at the St Nicholas Arena in New York. They would invite teenagers to come along and hear David preach.

`But where will you find the money to pay for the hire of the Arena?' asked David. `It must cost thousands of pounds.'

`Don't worry,' said a man in a smart suit. `I'll take care of everything.'

At first, David wasn't sure whether the man was just a crank, but he later discovered he was in fact an attorney by the name of Benignano Delgado. Mr Delgado told David he would pay for the hire of the Arena himself. And when David saw how much cash the attorney had in his pocket, all his doubts evaporated. Finance would be no problem.

When he got back home, David told Gwen about the plans that had been made. He was ecstatic.

`When's this rally going to be then?' asked Gwen.

`The second week in July.'

`The same week that the baby's due,' said Gwen.

David had forgotten all about it. What was he to do?

Gwen told him to go ahead with the rally. He would probably be more use there than he would be pacing up and down outside the delivery room. He thought she was probably right, but he couldn't help feeling guilty. How could you forget the date when your own baby is due to be born? What sort of a father was he?

David felt bad about being away from home but Gwen insisted that he should go ahead with the rally. She would be fine without him.

In the months preceding the rally, the preparations took up most of David's time. He was concerned that the congregation might take exception to his spending so much of his working time on trips to New York, but they had become just as keen as he was, having heard so much about the problems and needs of the young people in the city.

There were so many things for him and the other organizers to do before the rally took place: publicity materials to get ready, music to choose, ushers to recruit and counsellors to train so that there would be people available on the night to help anyone who wanted to make a commitment.

But, of course, the most important thing was to get lots of young people to come along to the rally. The Arena held seven thousand people and there were to be five evening meetings. That meant they needed to attract thirty-five thousand young people! No easy task!

David knew that receiving an invitation to the meeting was a big challenge to young people from the poor areas of New York, and it wasn't just because it could change their lives. It might seem like no big deal for a youngster to cross the town to attend a meeting, but it wasn't viewed that way in the roughest parts of the city. It was a dangerous undertaking to go through a part of the city that was enemy territory.

To counteract this problem, members of the churches arranging the rally went out and told the gang members that special arrangements had been made to transport them there. Buses would come and take them from the safety of their own patch straight to the venue.

The youngsters had other fears as well though. They were being asked to sit in a big hall that was packed full with their sworn enemies – and who knew what might happen if tempers rose? There could be one almighty gang fight. But David sensed that they were also afraid deep down they might lose control – that the cool façade they had carefully built up over the years might crumble and they would lose face by crying in front of their friends.

Once all the arrangements had been made and everyone who needed to had been told about the meetings, there was really nothing more that David could do. It was now a matter of waiting and praying for the rally to be a success.

It was an exciting time for David, and he felt invincible. No matter what obstacle lay in his path, he would overcome it. It was as if the hand of God was upon him. But, in all the excitement of planning for the rally, something happened that tested David to the limit and made him doubt the strength of his beliefs.

One weekend he was in a small town where

he was supposed to be leading some meetings for a young minister. But when he arrived at the parsonage he saw an ambulance speeding away from the house. According to one of the neighbours, it was the minister, his wife and their small child who had gone off in the ambulance. He said the child had been involved in a serious accident. David rushed to the hospital to see if he could help the family in any way.

The young minister was glad to have someone to talk to as he was deeply shocked by what had happened. When he heard the full story, David was appalled at the terrible tragedy that had befallen this godly man and his family.

The young minister explained that he had been dashing out of the house in a hurry because he was late for a funeral service. He got into his car and set off not realizing that his own child was playing underneath the vehicle. The car had run over the child, who was now fighting for his life in intensive care. Tyre marks were visible on the baby's face where the wheels had run over it.

David felt helpless. He was used to consoling the bereaved, but what could he possibly say to this unfortunate man? Not only was his child suffering terribly, but he was tortured by guilt because it was he who had caused the injuries.

The child later died of his injuries and the parents were devastated. David was also deeply affected by the tragedy. Horrified that such a thing could have happened to a Christian family and an innocent child, he found himself wondering how God could have allowed it. And he was filled with fears for the safety of his own family.

He couldn't say whether the tragedy had been a punishment from God or a test of the family's faith, although both those reasons had crossed his mind. All he did know was that he never, never wanted anything so terrible to happen to his own children. He found himself praying to God, asking Him to spare his children's lives.

It's possible that his anxiety was heightened by the impending birth of his third child. He was torn between his desire to be there for the delivery and his fear that something bad might happen to the baby if he disobeyed God's wishes and backed out of the rally.

He no longer saw God as his loving Father. Instead he was a cruel and vengeful tyrant who had to be feared and obeyed. And it didn't seem possible to do his duty to God and also do his duty to his wife and family.

Day after day, David cried bitter tears and agonized over what he should do. All the time his mind was tormented with fears and forebodings and he remembered again and again the agony of the young pastor and his wife. Time and time again he questioned his own motives for going to New York and tried to discover what God really wanted. But the more he tried to think things out, the more confused and anxious he became.

Then one day he suddenly saw things clearly again. David stood watching his children as they slept. Seeing their faces, he thought about how much he loved them and how he could never let them go or let anything happen that would harm them.

Out of the blue he heard God's voice reassuring him. `Of course you won't let your children go, David, and I will never let you go either. I love you even more than you love your children. There's nothing for you to fear.'

Everything was all right again. He knew that now. He could go to New York and trust that God would take care of Gwen and the children. Nothing bad would happen to them just because he was away. And the new baby would be fine. It really would be fine.

CHAPTER FIVE

Standing up for Jesus

It was the second week of July 1958 and the rally was proving to be a disappointment. Everyone had worked so hard to make it a success, but things didn't seem to be working out. Attendances had been much poorer than expected. Night after night David found himself speaking to a virtually empty Arena. The previous night, the fourth night of the rally, there had only been a hundred people in the audience. One hundred seats full and six thousand nine hundred empty.

David wouldn't have minded if the hundred people who were there had been responsive, but none of them seemed to be taking him seriously. He found it a trial to have to go out in front of these youngsters night after night, to put up with their giggling, their larking around, their obscene comments, to watch helplessly as rival gang members shouted out threats to one another and fights broke out.

He was beginning to think he and the other organizers had made a big mistake. Maybe they'd overreached themselves by taking on such a big project? Maybe David just didn't have what was needed to attract these kids from the New York gangs and hold their attention? His experience and culture were totally foreign to them.

It might have been better for everybody if he'd stayed in Philipsburg and been there to support Gwen when the baby was born. Here in New York he only seemed to be wasting everybody's time and money.

`What am I doing wrong, Lord?' the preacher prayed as he got into his car and set off for the Ortez apartment. `You'll have to tell me. I really don't know what else I can do.'

His answer came immediately, and from an unexpected source – a young gang leader named Jo-Jo whom David had befriended. Jo-Jo was the President of the Coney Island Dragons and he had lived on the streets for quite some time. But now, like David, he was staying with the Ortez family.

`The trouble with you, Preacher, is you're trying too hard.'

David was startled. Jo-Jo had hit the nail on the head. It was as if the young man had been reading his thoughts.

`What do you mean, Jo-Jo?' he asked.

`I mean this rally. Trying to speak to the kids. Why don't you just ease up?'

Jo-Jo was right. It wasn't David's job to cajole and persuade the young people to respond to God. If they did, it would be because God had opened up their hearts. It was God who would make things happen, not him.

`Thank you,' said David. `I'll try to do that.'

He smiled at his young companion. Maybe things weren't so bad after all?

The following evening, David arrived at the Arena with a real sense of anticipation. One reason for his raised spirits was the good news he had received in the early hours of the morning. There had been a telephone call to let him know that Gwen had had their baby. He was a fine, ten-pound baby boy and both mother and baby were doing well. He didn't need to worry about them any longer.

To David's delight he also found that the attendance was much better that night. As he watched the young people arrive and take their seats, his adrenaline was beginning to flow. It was as if God had already responded to his prayers. Before he'd even stepped onto the platform David knew that tonight would be different.

The meeting was due to start at seven thirty, and it had been arranged that the buses would pick up gang members at about seven o'clock. The bus drivers weren't used to dealing with youngsters as tough as these, and many of them found the journey to the Arena an ordeal, especially the one who had to transport the Mau Maus.

The Mau Maus had very little respect for authority and did their best to give the bus driver a rough ride. How on earth was he to cope with fifty aggressive gang members who were all drinking, smoking and shouting at the tops of their voices? It was as if they were deliberately trying to rile him with their foul language and unruly behaviour.

At the Arena it was the ushers' turn to tremble. They were volunteers from the churches which had organized the rally, but tonight's audience was a far cry from the orderly church congregations they were used to. The Mau Maus and the other gang members had no intention of doing as they were told. If they were going to attend the preacher's meeting, it would be on their own terms.

Fortunately, David had already given the Mau Maus preferential treatment. He had reserved some of the best seats in the Arena for the Mau Maus and their friends the Chaplains. By the time the Mau Maus arrived, the Chaplains were already in their places and they shouted to .the Mau Maus to come over and join them.

The chief usher looked nervously at David as the fierce looking young men strode in with their double M jackets, Tyrolean caps and canes. Should he try to stop them from taking the reserved seats?

`It's all right,' said David. `Those seats are for them. They're my special guests, the Mau Maus.'

The gang members pushed their way to their places at the front of the hall and the seats reverberated as their canes clanged against the metal.

David and the others then came onto the stage and took their seats with some trepidation. It was one thing to preach in an Arena that was nearly half empty, but it was quite another to be faced with several thousand gang members who were all intent on causing as much disruption as possible.

Never before had David addressed such an unruly audience. The Mau Maus and the Chaplains, and their rivals the Bishops and the GIs, were whistling, stamping their feet, shouting and banging their canes on the floor. But it wasn't just the noise that David found alarming. It was the possibility that serious trouble could break out at any minute. These gangs hated each other and were spoiling for a fight.

The manager of the Arena was worried too. If a fight did break out it would be pandemonium in the hall and he didn't think anyone would be able to do much about it. Maybe they should call the police before the situation became even more tense?

`No,' said David. `I think that would only inflame the situation. Let's wait and see if they quieten down by themselves once the meeting gets under way.'

So the meeting commenced, but David's optimism appeared to be misplaced. When the organist played, he was ridiculed, and gang members and scantily dressed teenage girls got up and danced on their seats. Their movements were suggestive and the mood in the hall was a far cry from the godly atmosphere that David was aiming for. How could anyone possibly listen to the Word of God with all this going on?

He had hoped that the singer, Mary Arguinzoni, might be able to quieten down the audience, but instead the poor girl was subjected to a barrage of rude remarks and sexual allusions. One young man even stood up and did an Al Jolson impersonation in the middle of her song, which made the audience even wilder.

The brave young woman struggled on, but hardly anyone could hear her above the tumult. As soon as she got to the end of her song, David signalled to her to come off stage. It was up to him to try to deal with them. He had no idea how he was going to get their attention though. This crowd was in no mood to listen to a serious message.

As if to underline this point, Nicky's strangulated voice rang out. `What do you think you're doing, Preacher? Are you gonna convert us all?'

The Mau Maus laughed uproariously. Nicky was pleased. He had stolen the show and shown that he could still control them. This skinny preacher was no threat to Nicky Cruz. He still had the Mau Maus eating out of his hand.

David took a deep breath and got on with what he had to say.

72

`We're going to do things a little differently tonight,' he said, looking straight at the Mau Maus. `I'm inviting the Mau Maus to take up the offering for us. We'll need six of you.'

Asking the Mau Maus to collect the offering! It was preposterous! Suddenly the audience began to pay attention. This man must be crazy to trust the Mau Maus with anything, never mind a large sum of money.

Nicky and some of his fellow gang members stood up and made their way to the stage where they were each handed an empty ice cream carton.

David gave them their instructions. `When you've finished, I'd like you to go behind that curtain there and come up onto the stage.' They glanced at the curtain and then gave each other knowing looks. Above the curtain was a big sign saying `Exit'. All they had to do was take the money and run.

Nicky made sure that the audience gave generously. He had quite a reputation throughout the city for his ruthless cruelty and nobody wanted to get on the wrong side of Nicky Cruz. If he thought anyone was being stingy, all he had to do was show them his knife and the terrified person would instantly produce some more money.

Now all the collection bearers had to do was pass through the curtains and they'd be gone. Out into the night, with a lot more money than they had when they arrived. Easy money.

David had sussed their intentions, but he had been determined to give them a chance to behave like decent human beings. If he didn't take them seriously, how could he expect them to listen to his message? He kept his eyes lowered and tried to avoid looking at the boys as they went through the curtain. He knew he was taking a terrible risk. If they did run off with all the money, there would be pandemonium in the Arena.

Nicky was also keeping a close watch on the boys who were carrying the collection. Out of the corner of his eye, he saw one of his helpers pocketing a twenty dollar bill. `Put that back,' he snapped. `We're going to give the preacher his money – all of it.'

The boys filed onto the stage and the shocked spectators started to boo and hiss at them. Clearly the audience was disappointed that the Mau Maus had wasted this chance to get one over on the preacher. What did they think they were doing, acting chicken like that?

David, however, was overjoyed. His faith in Nicky had paid off.

`Thank you,' he said, as Nicky handed over his carton of money. `I knew I could rely on you.'

The audience quietened down for David's sermon, but in spite of that he didn't feel confident about the effect he was having on the young people there. He sensed that his message wasn't reaching them, and he didn't know why. He had prepared well, and he certainly wasn't lacking in commitment. So why was there such an insurmountable barrier between himself and his listeners?

He carried on speaking for a quarter of an hour, then suddenly he got a response – but not the sort that he'd been hoping for. He was at the point in his sermon where he was explaining that we all ought to love one another, even people from a different race or culture from ourselves, when one of the gang boys leapt to his feet.

`Love those dagos? You must be out of your mind!' said the young man. `Look,' he said, pulling up his shirt, `who do you think gave me this scar?'

`And one of them shot me,' said a boy from the Hell's Burners, showing off his bullet wound. `How the hell do you expect me to love the nigger who did this?'

One of the Chaplains started to make his way across the Arena, kicking over chairs in his haste. The atmosphere was full of hatred and it was clear that if the mood didn't change soon David would have a full-scale rumble on his hands right there in the hall. How was he to preach about God's love in these circumstances? The boy had been right. It was a crazy thing to do.

However, when the preacher opened his mouth to speak, things started to make sense again.

`Maybe we can't love other people by ourselves. But we can if God gives us His love,' he said quietly. `We can't change ourselves, but God can.'

He was feeling calmer now that he had remembered that he didn't have to rely on his own efforts. There was no need for him to try so hard. It was God who would come into the lives of these teenagers and transform them.

He bowed his head and began to pray silently. `It's up to you, Lord. I'm handing tonight over to you so you can do what you want with these boys and girls. Your will be done, Lord.'

Yes, God was in control, whatever the outcome of the rally.

Gradually, imperceptibly, the commotion gave way to silence and David could hear the sound of someone sobbing. He looked up and saw that it was Israel. Then another person began to cry, followed by another and yet another. It was as if the Holy Spirit was sweeping through the auditorium, touching the young people's hearts.

`God is here with us in this room,' proclaimed David. `He's come to give you a new future. If you want a new life, now's the time to say so. I want you to get up now and come to the front.'

Straightaway Israel stood up and urged his gang members to accompany him.

`I'm going forward. Who's going to join me?'

Nicky responded. `I will.' He strode towards David, followed by more than two dozen Mau Maus. Thirty members from the other gangs also went to the front.

`The meeting's over,' said David. `Come downstairs to the dressing room if you'd like to speak to one of our counsellors.'

The gang members followed David along the corridor that led to the dressing room, and when they poured into the room the volunteers from the churches wondered how on earth they would cope with so many people. Interestingly enough, David noticed that only three of the new converts were girls. The girls had been more antagonistic than the boys.

A few gang girls had been hanging around the corridors, and they shouted out remarks as David was leading the boys to see the counsellors. One girl had pulled up her blouse to reveal a bare breast and she called to them. `You go in there and you won't see this any more.'

David couldn't understand why the girls were being so hostile, but Nicky had an explanation. `They're just jealous,' he said. `They don't know about real love.'

David nodded. What Nicky said made sense. These poor girls were so insecure that they'd do anything to hang on to what little love they had, even if it was only a pale imitation of the real thing.

He had to admit he was surprised at the way Nicky was acting. Could this be the same boy who had committed so many dreadful crimes? The boy who was feared throughout New York? The boy who had threatened to kill him?

As if he had been reading David's thoughts, Nicky turned to David and grinned from ear to ear.

`I'm giving my heart to Jesus, David. I really am.'

In the dressing room, the new converts were quickly assigned their respective counsellors who explained more about the new life that God was offering them. `So many new lives today,' thought David, remembering his own newborn son back in Philipsburg.

David was dealing with Nicky and Israel himself. He got the gang leaders to kneel on the floor in front of him.

`I'm going to say a prayer for you both,' he said. He placed his hands on their heads and tears ran down the boys' faces.

`It's all right,' said David. `Let it all out. Tell God how you feel.'

Nicky prayed a very simple prayer, but the words came straight from his heart. `O God, come into my life and change me, please change me. I'm tired of this life that I've been living.'

Listening to him, David could feel tears welling up in his own eyes as well. It had been quite a night.

The preacher led the two boys to another room. `Come with me and I'll give you each a Bible. He took some pocket sized Bibles out of a box and offered them to the boys.

`Here. Take some for the other Mau Maus as well.'

`Can't we have these big ones?' asked Nicky, lifting an extra large edition from another box. `That way everyone will see them and they'll know that we're Christians now.'

David went to bed that night on a real high, delighted that the meeting had been so fruitful. At last there was hope for boys like Nicky and Israel. But to his consternation, he was wakened early next morning by Mrs Ortez. There was a telephone call for him – from the police.

`Do you know the Mau Mau gang, Mr Wilkerson?'

`I do. Why do you ask?'

`We've got some of them here at the Auburn Street Police Station. I think you'd better come over.'

`I'll be right with you,' said David, suddenly fearful for his new converts. Surely they hadn't gone and gotten themselves into trouble already!

David arrived at the police station and found several of the gang members there, including Nicky and Israel, with the police lieutenant. There was a pile of guns lying on the counter beside them.

`What's the problem, Officer?' he asked.

`Just one minute please, sir.'

The lieutenant quickly assembled all his officers.

`There's no problem, Mr Wilkerson,' he said. `I just want to shake your hand. For years we've had nothing but trouble from these boys. But this morning a whole bunch of them trooped in here. Do you know what they wanted?'

David shook his head, bewildered.

`They wanted us to autograph their Bibles.'

`Look, Davie,' said Nicky, opening his extra large Bible. `Here's the lieutenant's autograph.'

`I don't know what you did, but it sure worked,' said the lieutenant. `Any time you need some help, just let us know.'

David thanked the lieutenant warmly and he and his happy throng of Mau Maus left the police station and walked out into the grey New York streets. Somehow they didn't seem quite so gloomy that morning.

CHAPTER SIX

Decision time

The rally was over, David's visits to New York had stopped and he was enjoying being back in Philipsburg again. It was green and fresh out in the country, and he especially enjoyed sitting in the garden with Gwen and the new baby. The dirty streets of New York and the poverty and deprivation of city life seemed a million miles away.

They were never far from his thoughts, though. The pastor continued to minister diligently to his parishioners, but, if the truth were told, his heart was still in New York with Nicky and Israel and all the other youngsters he'd got to know.

In Philipsburg, people were beginning to notice that he no longer seemed so enthusiastic about his ministry there. Gwen had warned him about it, and the subject had even been raised by one of the parishioners.

David felt guilty about it. He'd been doing his best to hide his real feelings, but obviously he hadn't managed to hide them well enough. This half-hearted commitment wasn't fair on his family, and it certainly wasn't fair on his congregation. They deserved one hundred per cent of his attention. And if he couldn't give it to them because of his attachment to New York, well, maybe he was in the wrong place?

He had to be sure, though. Moving to New York would be a big disruption for Gwen and the children. They were happy in Philipsburg. It was a pleasant place and they had a nice home, plenty of fresh air, security. If only youngsters like Nicky and Israel had grown up in the countryside, perhaps their lives might have turned out differently.

He didn't feel ready to take the plunge, but he had to do something. So in February 1959, a year after he had hit the headlines by getting himself thrown out of the Farmer murder trial, he took another step on his journey.

`I think I'll go back to New York for a visit,' he said to Gwen, who was not in the least surprised. `Just for one night.'

*   *   *   *   *   *

David felt excited as he drove into Brooklyn and recognized familiar streets which were piled with snow, as they had been when he made his first foray into the city the previous year. His feelings for the city hadn't changed either. He still felt close to it.

Getting out of his car onto the slippery streets of Fort Greene, he wondered if the people he had got to know would be the same – or would they have changed in the twelve months that had elapsed ? Would they remember him? And were the converts from the rally keeping their faith? He hoped and prayed that they would be, that they really would be living a different kind of life.

`Don't you know us, Davie?' said a man's voice. David looked up and saw before him two smart and healthy looking black soldiers. They looked familiar but at first he couldn't place them. Then he remembered.

`Buckboard! Stagecoach! Is it really you?'

`You bet.'

`I hardly recognized you. You look so well.'

They explained to David that they had left the gang after their conversion and now they were thrilled to be soldiers. Not many boys from their neighbourhood were able to pass the tests for admission to the army.

David liked Buckboard and Stagecoach and seeing them again he realized how much he had missed them. He felt as if he had been away from the city far too long.

One very important thing he had to do was to look for Nicky and Israel and find out what they had been up to since he last saw them. He didn't think that would be too difficult. In fact, he very soon bumped into a boy who knew them.

`They found religion, and Nicky's got it real bad. He wants to be a preacher.'

David was stunned. Nicky a preacher! He must find him and ask if it was true. Maybe he could help him somehow?

The transformation in Nicky was amazing. Gone was the tough, cruel expression on his face and the fear in his eyes. Instead David saw a youngster who was happy and relaxed and full of life.

Hearing Nicky bubbling over with plans for the future, David had a brilliant idea. `Nicky, in a few weeks' time I'll be talking to a church group in Elmira about the problems that young people have in the cities. Why don't you come along with me?'

Elmira, the city where Luis Alvarez had been jailed after the Farmer trial. Where was the boy now? David had no idea. But remembering the terrible plight of Luis Alvarez reassured him that it was right for Nicky to tell the church people his story, shocking though it was. The young people of New York were in desperate need of help.

Yes, they were desperate. Even when boys like Nicky were converted, they were still not safe if they had to carry on living in the midst of violence and gang warfare, as David was soon to discover.

One night not long before his engagement at Elmira, Nicky was attacked by a member of the Apache gang whom the Mau Maus had kidnapped, burned with cigarettes and beaten. It had been the Mau Maus' way of punishing him for attacking one of their boys.

This time, however, the Apache had a knife

and he thrust it towards Nicky's heart. It was only Nicky's quick reactions and fighting skill that saved his life. He instinctively reached for the blade which went into his hand instead of his chest. Then he pulled the ariel off a nearby car and used it to defend himself. It was a bitter fight, but Nicky won. In the old days he would have killed or maimed his rival, but on this occasion he had mercy on the boy and allowed him to get away.

Blood was pouring from the stab wound on Nicky's hand and he was getting weaker by the minute. But with help from one of the Mau Maus and Israel's mother, he managed to stagger to the nearest hospital where he underwent an emergency operation.

The meeting at Elmira was only one day after Nicky had been discharged from hospital. It was a six hour drive from New York City. David went on ahead, and one of the Christians who had befriended Nicky was to drive him there to meet David at two p.m. He was also bringing along a Puerto Rican boy who was to interpret what Nicky said at the meeting as Nicky's English was barely understandable.

David introduced Nicky to the audience with some private misgivings. He was afraid that these decent people might be so appalled by the violence and depravity in Nicky's life that they would miss the real point of why David had brought him there to tell his story. The country preacher wanted them to understand that it was the terrible environment in which boys like him were brought up and the poverty and the hopelessness of their situation which caused them to behave in this way.

However, Nicky told his story simply and directly and people warmed to him. He explained how he had been brought up by spiritualist parents and that even when he was a child he was always in trouble. He was fascinated by blood and enjoyed being violent, especially if his victims were weak and helpless.

But when he became vice-president of the Mau Mau gang, he had the weapons to inflict even more violence and had become ruthless. For years his life had been filled with stabbings, armed robbery and vicious gang fights.

He had been a tough guy and all the people in his neighbourhood had been scared of him, but he was the one who was frightened when one day he encountered a skinny preacher named David Wilkerson.

Then came the meeting at the Arena and for the first time in his life Nicky realized that someone trusted him. There was a chance for him to live a new life in spite of all the terrible sins he had committed.

Nicky spoke powerfully and, strangely enough, his voice no longer sounded strangled as it usually did. Today it rang out clear and strong.

The experience of speaking at Elmira was a breakthrough for Nicky. Now that he had seen he could speak in a way that engaged people, his cherished dream that he could train to be a preacher didn't seem so unlikely after all. And David was determined he would do all he could to help him. For a start, the collection that was taken up that night at Elmira would help to pay for Nicky to go to Bible School.

A few months later David received a letter from the Latin American Bible Institute at La Puente in California. Both Nicky and Angelo Morales had been accepted for training. David was overjoyed. It seemed that his work in New York was bearing fruit at long last.

But the following spring, David was jolted out of his complacency by a piece of terrible news. Israel was in prison on a murder charge. It was a bitter blow for the preacher. The other converts were doing well, so why had Israel failed to stay on the straight and narrow? He remembered how excited Israel had been on the night of the rally when he went around showing everyone how many times his name was in the Bible he'd been given.

David went to visit Israel's mother who explained to him that Israel had been working hard at school and getting on well. However, when the gang got together again, he had been drafted into it. Apparently it was very difficult for a boy to resist the draft, because anyone who did would be beaten up and might eventually be killed by gang members. This gang had, in fact, tried to shoot Israel several times before he eventually joined them out of fear for his life.

One night in December, Israel and four other boys were involved in a fight in which a member of the South Street Angels, a rival gang, was killed. Apparently it wasn't Israel who had actually done the shooting, but because he was involved in the incident he was arrested. He pleaded guilty to second degree murder and was given a five-year jail sentence.

David was full of guilt and despair that such a thing could have happened to Israel when he had made such a promising start in his Christian life. He spent many hours going over and over events in his mind and trying to work out how the situation could have been avoided.

`Where did I go wrong, Gwen?' he asked his wife one evening. `Israel needed me and I've let him down so badly. But what could I have done differently?'

`You did what you could, Davie. There's nothing else you could have done to keep an eye on Israel from such a distance.'

That was it. No matter who he spoke to, they always said the same. The problem was that David was going to New York and converting these boys then leaving them alone to cope with their new life with all the old difficulties and pressures of their environment. If he was really going to help them, it wasn't enough to preach the gospel. He had to provide some sort of follow-up as well.

On David's fifth anniversary as pastor of his church in Philipsburg, he stood in the pulpit.

`My family and I have had five wonderful years here with you in this town and we appreciate your friendship. But now I am clear that God has work for us elsewhere. We are leaving Philipsburg straight away.'

CHAPTER SEVEN

___

Stepping out in faith

The service was over and all the members of the
congregation had said goodbye and gone their
separate ways. David ambled back to the
parsonage and closed the door behind him with
a sigh of relief. He was glad to be back home in
the security of his own four walls.

He'd felt such a mixture of emotions in church
that morning. There was a feeling of relief that
he'd finally responded to God's prompting and
made the decision to quit his job. But there was
sadness, too, at the thought of leaving all the
dear people who'd been so kind to him and the
pleasant little country town where he and his
family had spent five happy years.

There was tremendous excitement, though, at
the prospect of moving to New York where he
felt he belonged. He wanted to be there. He
knew there was a real need for him there. But at
the same time there was fear. Fear that came in
waves over his whole body and knotted his
stomach.

`I really am stepping into the unknown,' he
said to Gwen as they sat and sipped coffee
together. `Here I am giving up my job and our
home and I've no idea how I'll manage to

support us or where we'll all live. How on earth do you put up with me?'

`Honey, you're doing what you believe God wants, and I wouldn't have you do things any differently,' smiled Gwen. `We'll manage, just you wait and see. If this is really God's will, He'll show us the way.'

He did, that very afternoon. During the next few hours several people telephoned to arrange for David to come for speaking engagements and meetings all over the country. By the end of the day his diary contained twelve weeks of appointments.

`Well, that solves our money worries for a while,' said David, amazed at how quickly things had fallen into place. `But that still leaves the problem of where the five of us are going to live. We'll have to move out of the parsonage pretty soon, you know.'

`That's all taken care of,' said Gwen. `I've already had a word with my folks and they're going to let us use some rooms in their house. There won't be enough space for our furniture, but we can store that. At least we'll have a roof over our heads.'

* * * * * *

When he visited churches in other parts of the country, David took every opportunity to tell the people he met about New York and the terrible problems he had witnessed among the young people there. One day in the winter of 1960 he was discussing this with Reginald Yake, a pastor in Irvington, New Jersey.

Mr Yake was very interested in what he heard about the situation in New York and asked many questions about what the young people needed. David answered them as best he could, sharing his own vision of what might be done in the poorest areas.

`It sounds as if there's a real need for someone to work with these young people,' said Mr Yake. `I have some friends who may be able to help you. Let me see what I can do.'

A meeting was eventually arranged in a church run by of one of Mr Yake's friends, and several church leaders came along to it. David told them how he had got involved with the New York teenagers and outlined his ideas for helping them.

`What are we waiting for?' said someone. `If this is what the teenagers really need, let's get a move on and make it happen.'

There and then, the church leaders founded an organization to work with young people and gave it the title `Teen-Age Evangelism'. David was to be its director and its only paid employee, and one of the church members, Paul DiLena, was appointed secretary and treasurer in his absence.

It was decided that the organization would

need a budget of twenty thousand dollars for the first year's work, so they allocated themselves this sum. But it only existed in theory. In reality they had no money at all.

Soon David found himself pounding the grey streets of New York yet again. This time he had something specific to do. He'd been given the task of finding some offices that Teen-Age Evangelism could use for it's headquarters.

How strange, he thought to himself. It's only two years since I came to New York to try to help the boys in the Farmer trial. A smile crept across his lips as he remembered what he was like when he made his first few visits. I knew nothing about the seamy side of New York in those days, absolutely nothing. To think I even slept in my car! That shows just how naive I was.

He checked the address that he'd copied onto a piece of paper – 1865 Victory Boulevard. There it was. The neighbourhood wasn't up to much, he had to admit. But the offices might be OK. He'd been told that there were three rooms which should be adequate for such a small organization as his.

When he went inside the building, he found that the rooms were dingy and in need of a good clean. But they were cheap, which was the main thing. After all, as the only paid member of staff, he was the only one who had to spend much time in them.

Spending time in New York. That reminded him of another sensitive subject. Now that he was going to be based in New York, he and Gwen would have to live apart. The arrangement was far from ideal, but there didn't seem to be anything he could do about it for the time being.

Eventually they'd find somewhere in New York where they could all live together, but he and Gwen had decided to postpone any move until the end of the school year for the sake of their two daughters. Until then, David would be sleeping on a camp bed in the office. On his modest salary, he couldn't afford to stay anywhere else.

`Never mind,' he consoled himself. `At least in a place like this I'll have plenty of opportunity to pray. There won't be anything else to distract my attention here. No home comforts or late night television.'

David settled down to his new job very quickly. Thanks to the generosity of New York's Assemblies of God churches, he soon had funding for two experimental projects. The first, Operation Saturation, provided hand-outs for high school pupils in deprived areas of the city. They contained a biblical perspective on many subjects which the young people would find relevant, including alcohol, drugs, sex and violence.

The second project, which was more

ambitious, used television to communicate with the young people. The television stars were themselves boys and girls who had been in trouble but had managed to get their lives back on course again. Each week one of the youngsters would tell his or her story and the others sang together in a choir. The show really appealed to the city's teenagers and was a great success.

One thing which the organization hadn't fully realized was how expensive the television shows were going to be. It costs a great deal of money to produce a television programme, and by the end of the first thirteen week series Teen-Age Evangelism had four and a half thousand dollars of unpaid debts.

A meeting was called to try to resolve the situation, but as there seemed to be no way out of this particular financial crisis, it looked as if the project was doomed. Even though the youngsters loved the programmes, even though they sent in their pocket money to keep the show going, Teen-Age Evangelism simply couldn't afford to broadcast for another thirteen weeks.

`Hold on a minute,' said a stranger at the back of the room. He introduced himself as a minister in the Dutch Reformed Church, the Reverend Harald Bresden.

`I like your shows very much,' he said, `and I hope it won't be necessary for you to cancel them. Before you do anything, I'd like you to have a word with a friend of mine, Chase Walker.'

David wasted no time. The very next day he went along with Harald Bresden to Chase Walker's office in Manhattan. Mr Walker, a magazine editor, listened sympathetically while David explained the predicament the organization found itself in.

`How much money are you going to need?' he asked.

David hesitated. `Ten thousand dollars.' He was aware that it was a very large sum of money.

`Ten thousand dollars!' Chase Walker raised his eyebrows in amazement. `I'd love to help you with your project, but I'm afraid I just don't have that sort of money. Why did you think of asking me to help?'

`I don't know', admitted Harald. `It was a hunch I suppose. But my hunches are usually right. I'm sorry we've wasted your time.'

David and Harald were making their way down the corridor when they heard a voice calling them. It was Chase Walker again.

`Gentlemen, I've had an idea. Please come back in for a moment.' He ushered the two men back into his offices. `I just remembered something that happened to me this morning. I received a telegram from someone that I know,' said Mr Walker, passing the piece of paper over the desk.

David and Harald read it. The message was very short and simple. 'Disregard previous telegram. I will be at the Savoy Hilton Wednesday. W. Clement Stone.'

'Mr Stone is the president of an insurance company in Chicago. The strange thing is,' explained Mr Walker, 'I don't know what this previous telegram is that he's referring to. And I've no idea why he should tell me he'll be in town. We didn't have any plans to get together.'

David nodded, mystified. Chase Walker sat quietly for a moment thinking, then snatched a piece of paper and a pen from his desk.

'I'm writing you a letter of introduction,' he said as his pen flew across the page. 'I think you should go and see Clement Stone at the Savoy. Tell him I sent you.'

David and Harald wasted no time. They were soon at the Savoy where they found Mr Stone in his room, putting on his bow tie for dinner.

They handed him the letter of recommendation in which Chase Walker explained that David was doing great work with the city's teenagers but needed ten thousand dollars for his project. Mr Stone read it with a puzzled look on his face, then smiled at his two visitors.

'I'm afraid I'm due to meet someone in a few minutes,' said Mr Stone. 'But if you like, you can come in and talk to me while I'm getting ready.'

David did his best to tell Mr Stone about the work of Teen-Age Evangelism in the short time that was available. There was so much he could have said if only Mr Stone hadn't been in such a rush.

`I'm very sorry,' said Mr Stone, stopping David just as he was getting into his stride. `I really must go now. But I like the sound of what you're doing. I'll provide the ten thousand dollars that you need. Just send your bills to me.'

David could hardly believe his ears. Fifteen minutes with a total stranger and suddenly all their debts were being taken care of. And the television show, which was reaching so many young people, could carry on for another series. Yes, faith could certainly move mountains.

It was just as well. For even before the television project was complete, David was already making even bigger and better plans for Teen-Age Evangelism. Plans which would require large sums of money and a great deal of faith.

CHAPTER EIGHT

The next move

David was explaining his latest plan to the Central Committee of Teen-Age Evangelism.

`As you'll be aware, our work so far has been reaching large numbers of young people and the response has been excellent. Through Teen-Age Evangelism, we're giving many of the young people of New York the chance to begin a new life.' He paused, looked at the committee members who were listening intently.

`The problem is, what happens afterwards? What we're failing to do is provide them with an opportunity for face-to-face contact afterwards, when they're having difficulties in living this new life in their old environment. Many of them spend their everyday lives surrounded by violence, drugs, alcohol, and promiscuity. They're completely alone and without support. Their friends are usually still gang members, and the gangs put pressure on ex-members to rejoin – you may have heard how Israel was drafted back into a gang after his conversion.'

`I think we're fully in agreement with you that there is a problem,' said one of the committee members. `The question is, what do we do about it?'

`Here's my idea,' said David. `We buy a house

99

in one of the tougher areas of the city so that some of the most needy young people can come and stay in it for a while. We could take in drug addicts, alcoholics, gang members, teenagers with sexual problems. We could call the establishment Teen Challenge Center.'

`And who would work with all these young people? Wouldn't you require a lot of staff?' asked another committee member.

`I envisage there would be about a dozen full-time staff. They would be young Christians who are utterly committed to doing this sort of work. Of course, we wouldn't be able to pay them much.'

David remembered with some discomfort that money was the nub of the matter as had been the case in so many projects. He knew that it would cost a lot to set up and run the centre, no matter how little they paid the staff. And the organization usually only had about a hundred dollars in its account at any one time.

`Well, David, it sounds like a marvellous idea, but I don't think we're in a position to fund it at this particular time. May I suggest that we put it to one side until we're in a financial position to be able to do something about it?'

David smiled. `That sounds like the logical solution, and, in fact, it's the conclusion I came to myself after I'd been thinking about the project. But my wife, Gwen, chastised me for my lack of faith. She said that if I really believed in this plan, I should make a commitment to it first, then find the money afterwards.'

The committee was silent for a moment, then one by one they lent their support. By the time David left the meeting, Teen-Age Evangelism had made a firm commitment to set up the centre and David had been delegated to look for a suitable building for it.

He was getting used to going and looking at property. First he'd found an office for Teen-Age Evangelism, then only recently he'd acquired a small apartment not far from his office where he could live with Gwen and the children.

It was good to have his family around him again. It had been lonely living on his own and sleeping on a camp-bed in the office – even though he had been able to get a lot of praying done! And Gwen was such a support to him in his work, so full of good ideas.

How was he to find the right sort of building for the centre, though? One requirement was that it would have to be in Bedford-Stuyvesant where there was the greatest need for it. Obviously it had to be large enough to accommodate the young people who were going to be staying there and the staff who would look after them.

And David wanted it to have a friendly, homely feel – after all, many of the young people had never known the love and security of a real home.

David had always continued with his late-night prayer sessions, and it was during one of these, at two o'clock in the morning in December 1960 that he began to have a more precise idea of where he should be looking. The name Clinton Avenue came into his mind. It was as if he knew deep down that this was where Teen Challenge Center would be, even though he hadn't even seen the street.

But visit it he must, and so began the task of looking at properties on Clinton Avenue. The first house he looked at had one big advantage – at seventeen thousand dollars it was extremely cheap. But when David expressed a serious interest in buying it, the person who showed him round seemed to backtrack. Perhaps this wasn't the property for Teen-Age Challenge after all?

The second house was rather more expensive at thirty-four thousand, but as it was already a nursing home, it seemed like the perfect place to use for the centre. It had everything that David would need – offices, staff accommodation, even beds. The owner was even prepared to reduce his price, but when it came to signing the papers, David had cold feet. He wanted Teen Challenge Center to be a home from home, a warm and welcoming place, but this building seemed gloomy and institutional.

It was a member of the Teen-Age Evangelism board, Dick Simmons, who suggested the next house that they were to look at which was just across the road from the nursing home. It was an impressive looking Georgian house, but, unfortunately, it was even more expensive than the others. The asking price was sixty-five thousand dollars.

Dick unlocked the door and David stepped inside, expecting to see rooms that were every bit as grand as the exterior. But he couldn't believe his eyes. It was like a rubbish tip.

An elderly tramp had been squatting in the house and was rather eccentric in his habits. He had piled all the rooms high with all sorts of junk which he'd collected from the neighbours' dustbins – everything from old prams to jam jars. And everything inside the building was in need of repair as well, from the plaster to the water pipes.

David sighed, deeply disappointed that the building hadn't lived up to his expectations. He could see that it must have been a marvellous house in its heyday, but to make it habitable would be a mammoth task – and it wasn't one that he felt like taking on.

But Dick Simmons was convinced that this was the house God wanted them to buy. What's more, he managed to persuade the owner to reduce the price to forty-two thousand in view of the amount of renovation that would be required.

David was torn. He really didn't want to

waste precious time restoring the house to a habitable condition. He wanted to be in there, with everything ready, working with the kids who needed them. Surely that was more important than doing plumbing and decorating?

But if Dick was right and God did want them to have this particular house, he didn't want to stop his colleagues from going ahead with the purchase. If only he knew what was really God's will! He decided the only way was to put a fleece before the Lord.

He asked one of the pastors of the Glad Tidings Church if he might come and make an appeal to the congregation on Sunday afternoon. He would ask the Lord to provide the four thousand two hundred dollars that were needed for the deposit in one single afternoon. That would be quite a feat as it was more than twice as much as the church had ever managed to raise in any one appeal. And to make the task even more difficult, he would simply state the facts and avoid trying to tug on the listeners' heartstrings.

The Sunday David had chosen was the one before Christmas and the pastor had already warned him that he might not get much money because it was so close to Christmas and afternoons weren't a good time to ask for money. David was feeling a little shamefaced by now. He realized he was doing everything possible to try to stop the board from purchasing the building. But he had put out the fleece, so now he had to wait and see what would happen.

He told the congregation very simply what Teen-Age Evangelism was trying to do and explained what he needed. Then he went downstairs to wait in the basement where anyone who wanted to could come and bring him a donation towards the cost of the project.

For the first ten minutes nobody came at all and David was beginning to think that he would escape the dreaded renovation work. But then parishioners filed in one by one and gave what they could, everything from fourteen cents from one schoolboy to three hundred dollars from an adult. Everyone who donated money told him how much they believed in the work he was doing. They really wanted the centre to happen.

When they had all gone, David and his helpers counted the cash and cheques with bated breath. Would there be enough? If there wasn't David's fleece would have failed. He would have been shown that the building wasn't the right one and Teen-Age Evangelism would have to start looking for another property.

Finally they arrived at the grand total – four thousand four hundred dollars. Enough to pay the binder and two hundred dollars to spare. They could now go ahead and buy the house on Clinton Avenue. Teen Challenge Center was not just a dream any more.

One thing that did puzzle David was why

they had been given an extra two hundred dollars. Maybe it was asking too much to expect God to give them exactly the right amount, but all the same he did wonder about it. The enigma was solved a few days later when David found out that they would have to pay two hundred dollars in legal fees when they put down the binder. They hadn't allowed for this extra expenditure – but God had!

The binder had now been paid, but that still left twelve thousand dollars to find for the remainder of the down payment. The money for this was found fairly quickly. The congregation of a Long Island church donated three thousand dollars the following Sunday, after hearing David speak about the project. And not long afterwards another minister, Arthur Grave presented David with a blank cheque from his church. David was to fill in whatever sum was necessary for him to go ahead and buy the house.

They had done it. Although Teen-Age Evangelism usually only had a hundred dollars in its account, they'd managed to obtain the premises they needed. David had dreamt of a home where disturbed teenagers could come and be loved and break free from their addictions, and now that dream was to become a reality.

The organization was now the proud owner of 416 Clinton Avenue, which would be known as

Teen Challenge House. David couldn't wait for the day when the first troubled teenager would be welcomed and given food, shelter and Christian love.

But before anyone could come and stay in the house, there was a huge amount of work to be done to make it habitable. The first job was to clear the building of the rubbish with which the old tramp had cluttered up every room. David didn't know how they would ever manage such a colossal task.

`A working party. That's what we need,' said Gwen as she surveyed the huge piles of junk. `Why not get some of the teenagers to come and tackle it?'

Fifteen youngsters responded to the invitation to come and help and turned up one Saturday morning full of enthusiasm. But even they were daunted by the prospect of clearing out so much old rubbish. They had to climb over it to get anywhere, and they couldn't even see some of the doors because of the mass of rubbish that was piled up in front of them.

It was slow going, but bit by bit they managed to get the rubbish out onto the street where trucks from the Sanitation Department were waiting to take it away. The debris amounted to six whole lorryloads.

But that was only the start of their hard work. Now that the building was empty, it had to be cleaned, redecorated and repaired. A number of volunteers turned up from various of the churches to help with the decorating, but the more work everyone got through, the more they discovered there was to do.

Take the plumbing, for example. It was the middle of winter and some of the pipes in the old building had frozen. Others actually burst. So plumbers had to be called in to repair the damage – yet another expense that the organization hadn't bargained for. And there were legal requirements to be fulfilled as well. The authorities insisted that they install a sprinkler system, which cost five thousand dollars.

All this extra expenditure meant that more money had to be found from somewhere, so David and some of the other supporters had to take time off from the restoration work to go round the country fund-raising.

Another problem was what to put in the building once it was in a fit state to be used – the organization had no furniture, not even beds. However, by now a number of successful businessmen had learned about the project and were very generous in their support of it. One of these, Mr Simmons, was the president of a company that manufactured beds, and he very generously donated the twenty beds the Center required.

Money was, of course, essential, but David was wise enough to recognize that it was the people who would staff the Center who would be crucial to the success of the enterprise. He decided the staff ought to be young. They would work in the Center, but they would also venture out onto the streets to do outreach work in very dangerous conditions.

It was vital that the new recruits were committed Christians, as David knew of no special techniques for curing the drug addicts who would seek help from the Center. It was only Jesus who could transform damaged and desperate young people and give them hope of a better future.

The workers must also have engaging personalities so that the street kids would want to listen to them. They would have to be fearless, as they would be risking their lives working on the toughest streets of the city, and they must be strong enough to cope with the demanding nature of the work. Another important requirement was their willingness to work for only ten dollars a week as that was all the Center could afford.

Finding twenty young people who met all these requirements was a tall order.

`Do you really think we'll be able to get the young people that we need to staff the Center?' he asked Gwen one day.

As always, Gwen's faith reassured him. `Relax, honey. God knows what you need. I'm sure He's got everything in hand. Remember how He found us the money we needed when we had virtually nothing in the bank?'

Sure enough, the answer came, and much more quickly than David expected. Just at the stage when they needed to start recruiting staff, David received an invitation to give a lecture at a Bible College at Springfield in Missouri. When he went there he was delighted to discover that the college president fully supported the work of the Center.

`Teen Challenge is meeting a real need in New York', he addressed his students. 'I would go so far as to say that the work of David Wilkerson and his colleagues is the closest thing I have seen to the challenge of Apostolic times.'

David was delighted to hear the president's endorsement of the Center, but he hadn't fully realized how much practical support the college intended to provide for it. The president continued with his speech and the students sat and drank-in every word he said. David's description of life on the streets had been an eye-opener to them.

`The college will provide financial assistance to any student who wants to go and work on this important project but cannot afford to do so. All those interested should assemble in the school library in a few minutes' time where you will be able to meet Mr Wilkerson.'

Seventy of the students turned up at the library. David did his best to put them off by emphasizing all the dangers and hardships they would face. Working at Teen Challenge Center would be far from glamorous. They wouldn't feel like heroes when they were peeling potatoes or scrubbing the floor.

In spite of the grim picture he painted, not many of the students were deterred, and David eventually selected sixteen of them to come and work at the Center. The remaining four workers were recruited from a college in Tennessee.

Before long, David and Gwen were standing on the steps of 416 Clinton Avenue welcoming the new recruits. They watched as each of the students arrived, bright and eager, but a little fearful too. David had no doubt that this was God's will, but he knew it wouldn't be easy. There were still many challenges ahead both for them and for all the other staff of Teen Challenge Center.

CHAPTER NINE

`Give us this day our daily bread'

The new helpers at Teen Challenge Center had a lot to learn. If they were to go out onto the streets and speak to tough young people from the gangs, they had to have some idea why these teenagers behaved in the way they did. The ugly world of drug addiction and alcoholism, of murder, rape and sexual vices was not something they had encountered before in their sheltered lives.

Above all, they needed to understand how pitiful the homes were that these boys came from: overcrowded apartments which lacked basic amenities like running water, cookers and refrigerators. Often eight families would have to share a toilet and a water tap down the hallway. Teenagers were often only given a pittance to feed themselves, so it was not surprising that they became thin and malnourished.

Life in the slums was harsh and unrelenting, and it was hard enough to stay alive there, never mind fulfil one's potential. Coming from this sort of background, it was only natural that young people didn't hold home or family life in much esteem.

For the privilege of living in awful hovels,

occupants were charged twenty dollars a week. The Teen Challenge workers earned only ten dollars a week, so they understood what a struggle it must be for the boys' parents to pay such high rents.

`But why do they put up with it?' asked one of the helpers. `Why don't the families move somewhere else?'

David explained that the black people and Puerto Ricans didn't really have any choice as to where they lived. In New York there was a lot of racial prejudice and lots of landlords wouldn't rent them property. So they were forced to live in ghettos in these deplorable conditions.

Housing projects such as Fort Greene had been intended to provide decent accommodation for the slum dwellers, but in practice what happened was that those who could afford to moved away. This meant that the housing projects became filled with the poorest members of the population and the buildings soon fell into disrepair. One of the major problems was that there was no sense of community in the housing projects as the inhabitants didn't have any roots in the locality.

The Teen Challenge workers also had to learn about drug addiction and the terrible effects it had on people. The drug dealers targeted even young children by hanging around outside schools and offering a child a puff of marijuana.

Eventually they would introduce the individual to heroin, and after fifteen continuous days of using the drug, the user would be addicted. He would now have to find an average of twenty-five to thirty dollars a day to support his habit, which would usually cost between twenty-five to thirty dollars a day. Some addicts might require as much as a hundred dollars' worth of drugs a day.

One obvious way of finding money was to turn to crime; another was to start peddling drugs to other children. First the addict would have to introduce other young people to drugs and get them hooked – existing drug dealers wouldn't take kindly to anyone who poached their customers.

Each Teen Challenge worker would be given a particular area of responsibility. Some would specialize in working with addicts; others might concern themselves with the `Little People', the eight-, nine- and ten-year olds who hung around the gangs; while others would work with the `Debs', young girls who went around with gang members and were often sexually promiscuous.

David's young helpers risked their lives every day because they were spending time in the roughest areas of the city where even police officers would not venture alone. In these parts of the town, murders, assaults, violent robberies and rapes were regular occurrences.

Often there was no rational explanation for the violence. Addicts who were high on heroin might easily lash out with a knife for no reason whatsoever. The Teen Challenge workers were in a particularly dangerous position because the gang members and their girls saw them as a threat to their relationships. Their lives were so unstable that belonging to the gang was one of the few things that gave them a feeling of security.

David took some sensible precautions to ensure that the Teen Challenge workers were as safe as possible. If they were ministering on the streets they had to go out in teams of two or three, and they could only make contact with members of the same sex. They also had to rendezvous with their fellow workers at regular intervals.

But they very quickly had to learn to cope with foul language and harassment, and attacks did happen. In one incident, the girl, Linda Meisner, who worked with the Debs, was attacked by a boy with a knife. Fortunately the weapon only tore her dress. She was shaken but unharmed.

Not everyone was so lucky. A reformed gang member named Carlos went back to his former haunts to try to share his faith with the rest of the gang. He was stabbed in the ribs and nearly died. Fortunately, though, he did recover from his injuries and the attack didn't deter him from going out and preaching again.

The young people who went out from the

Center were obviously in no position to defend themselves against a violent attacker. They had no weapons and could not rely on brute strength to save them. All they could do was pray and hope that God would protect them if they ever got into a difficult situation.

They knew they were putting themselves in a dangerous position, but they didn't care. All they wanted to do was go out and share the gospel and bring hope to boys and girls who were less fortunate than themselves.

David was delighted with all the young people who came to work at the Center. He was amazed at the way in which they were utterly devoted to their work and serious about it without losing any of their freshness and vitality. This was a big plus as the street kids wouldn't have listened to them unless they saw that they had attractive, happy personalities.

The original recruits were soon joined by two new ones who brought particular pleasure to David. One day David saw a familiar face at the Center. It was Nicky Cruz. David had seen him take his first excited steps as a new Christian at the meeting in the Arena, and now it was a tremendous thrill to see how he had matured and developed in his Christian life. Nicky was a fully fledged minister now, and a married man as well. He proudly introduced his wife Gloria to David.

Both Nicky and Gloria were keen to work at

the Center. As Gloria was very fond of children, she wanted to get involved with the Little People, the eight-to-ten-year-olds who would end up getting into trouble and joining gangs when they grew older.

Nicky felt a vocation to work with the parents who lived in the roughest areas. Up till now David and his co-workers had been devoting all their attention to the young people themselves. Nicky thought this was a serious omission.

`The parents are so important, Davie. It doesn't matter how much you do for young people if all they have to go back to is a terrible home life.'

David agreed and was glad to have such a capable young man as Nicky to tackle this vital role.

Prayer and personal devotion formed the backbone of the workers' day at Teen Challenge Center. David felt that unless each of the staff members made time to pray and maintain a rich spiritual life, all their efforts would be in vain. Time was set aside for personal devotions after breakfast, then the whole group spent two hours in chapel from half-past nine to half-past eleven in the morning. There were also services in the evening between half-past seven and midnight.

At the Center, the staff took literally the line from the Lord's Prayer, `Give us this day our daily bread.' They lived a day at a time, never knowing where their next meal was going to come from, and literally praying for their supper. They ate whatever people donated, or if some money came in that was not destined for a particular purpose they bought food with it. But it was very much a hand-to-mouth existence which meant that they constantly had to rely on God to fulfil their every need.

One day everyone got up out of bed and found there was no food at all for them to eat that day. Twenty-five people to feed, no food and no money to buy any! That was a real test of their faith.

`How much will it cost to buy lunch and dinner for everybody?' asked David.

`Between thirty and thirty-five dollars, I reckon,' replied the Reverend Culver.

`There's only one thing to do, then,' said David. `We'd better go to the chapel right now and pray for food for today or for enough money to buy the food that we need.'

So everyone trooped along to the chapel, both the staff and the kids who'd been brought in off the streets. Hungry stomachs made sure that they prayed loud and hard for God to meet their needs. This was no polite, detached request. All the inhabitants of Teen Challenge Center were praying as if their lives depended on it.

In the middle of their fervent prayers, a member of the public walked into the chapel. At first nobody noticed her because they were all too busy praying, and the noise of their intercessions drowned out her knock at the door. But at long last she managed to attract David's attention.

`I'm very sorry to disturb you, but I need to talk to someone.'

David couldn't figure out why she'd come to Teen Challenge. She seemed to be beating about the bush as she began asking one question after another, but she did seem friendly and well-disposed towards the Center.

`What are you praying for right now?' she eventually asked him.

`We're praying for food or money to buy it. We got up this morning to find we had nothing to eat and we're all hungry.'

The lady seemed startled as if things were suddenly falling into place in her mind.

`Tell me, Reverend, what time did you start praying?'

`An hour ago,' replied David, puzzled.

`That's remarkable,' she said. `That's really remarkable.'

She went on to explain that about an hour before she had felt compelled to empty out the contents of her money box and bring the money to Teen Challenge. She'd never done anything like that before and she couldn't explain it. But she'd followed her urge. She handed over some money in an envelope to David.

`There's thirty-two dollars there,' she

announced. `I hope you'll find it useful. God bless you all.'

And with a smile and a handshake she was gone. David smiled. Their prayers had been answered, and more quickly than they'd imagined. Today they would eat after all.

The Teen Challenge Center approached all its money problems in the same prayerful way. Some people might have thought that the organization was imprudent to set up the Center with all the expenditure that was involved when it couldn't guarantee that it would be able to pay its way. It cost over a thousand dollars a week to run the Center.

But David didn't think they were being irresponsible. He had a different perspective. He remembered what Gwen had said before he decided to turn his dream into a reality. She had reminded him that he wasn't acting out of faith if he waited till he had the money he needed before going ahead with the project. No, if he had faith, he would commit himself to the project even though he had no idea where the money for it would be coming from.

And it had worked. He and his colleagues had found the premises and paid the initial mortgage payment even though they had started off with virtually no money in the bank. And although they generally had less than a hundred dollars in the bank, they eventually managed to pay every bill that came in, whether it was for plumbing repairs or food or clothes or printing costs.

Teenagers all over America did odd jobs to raise money to support the Center or made donations from their pocket money. Members of the public sent in cheques or brought along items of food. The staff literally never knew where their next penny was coming from.

It was scary at times, but David was sure it was good for them spiritually. Living the way they did, they constantly had to have faith in God and believe that He would supply whatever they needed. Life consisted of God-reliance rather than self-reliance.

Some bills caused more anxiety than others, though, particularly the large mortgage payments which were due from time to time. They had managed to obtain the money for the binder by appealing for funds, and had only managed to pay the rest of the down payment in the nick of time. If they hadn't got the money for the down payment, the Center would never have got off the ground.

Now another date was looming uncomfortably close – August 28th, 1961, the day they would have to make the second mortgage payment. It was only two weeks away. It was going to cost a lot of money – fifteen thousand dollars to be precise – and they didn't have anything laid aside for it. Finding thirty-two dollars for a day's food was one thing, but getting hold of fifteen thousand dollars quickly was a challenge of a different magnitude.

David was painfully aware that he had avoided thinking about the mortgage, but it was going to catch up with him now. Once the deadline arrived, he wouldn't be able to ignore it any longer. Nobody at the Center would. Teen Challenge Center was in a race against time – it had to find fifteen thousand dollars by August 28th or close down.

The days ticked by and David knew in his mind what a serious predicament they were in. Everything he had worked for, all the good work that had been done for the street kids could soon be at an end. He ought to be worried, but somehow he had a feeling in his gut that everything would be all right. It wasn't rational, but it was a deeply felt instinct.

He supposed he had some justification for feeling that way. Before, when the members of the organization had found themselves in a tight spot, something miraculous always happened to save them. Why couldn't the same thing happen now? But as day followed day it seemed less and less likely that Teen Challenge's problems would be solved so easily.

The Center continued with its daily régime of work and prayer, and all too soon the fateful day dawned. The second mortgage payment had to be made that very day by twelve noon, but it just didn't seem possible that it would happen.

After all, there were only fourteen dollars in the Center's bank account.

David listened as the clock struck twelve, and his heart sank with every chime. Maybe he had been too complacent. Maybe it had been wrong of him to expect God to bale him out if he wasn't doing enough to help himself. He had been irresponsible, and now the Center would suffer the consequences.

It just didn't seem fair. All the staff at the Center had worked so hard and it was a happy place. It was doing a lot of good. Anyone could see that it had made a difference to many of the boys and girls in the city. Surely God wouldn't abandon the Center now when He had been with it and blessed it all along?

Desperate, David spoke to Julius Fried, the organization's attorney. `If only there were something I could do!' sighed David. `If only we had a little more time!'

`I'll see what I can arrange for you,' said Julius. `But I can't promise anything. This really is a very serious situation.'

By the end of the day Julius had managed to arrange an extension. The lenders would give them until September 10th to come up with the money. But if they still hadn't received the payment by then, they would foreclose on the mortgage.

So they now had a little more time, but still David had no idea where the money was going to come from. So David did what he always did in a crisis. He turned to prayer. He got together all the young people who worked at the Center or used its facilities and told them to go to the chapel and give thanks that the Center is safe.

`You got the money then?'

`Not yet,' said David, aware of how crazy his idea was. `But we will. We'll have it by the tenth of September, I'm sure. We're just thanking God in advance.'

The board members also took practical steps to try to obtain the money that was needed. Every one of them spent hours on the telephone, calling people who had supported the Center in the past. Some people donated money, but it was peanuts in comparison to the fifteen thousand dollars that were needed.

Although the board members didn't have much money to show for all their fund-raising efforts, there were plenty of other indications that the Center was a success. The organization kept careful records of all the people with whom it dealt, and from these they could see that two and a half thousand people had become Christians as a result of their contact with the Center. In addition, hundreds of young people had stayed at the Center at some time or another. For most of them, going to the Teen Challenge Center had been a turning point in their lives, and they had found hope for the future.

It was all very encouraging, but there was still the problem of the outstanding mortgage payment. If they couldn't pay that by the new deadline, it wouldn't matter how much good they had done. Business was business and the mortgage lenders had a right to their money.

Harald Bresden picked up the telephone to ring Clem Stone in Chicago. He felt bad about asking him for money yet again when he had already given them so much. But he had to ask all the Center's supporters for help, even if he felt uncomfortable about it. He could hear the phone ringing at the other end, and he felt butterflies in his stomach.

`Hello, is that Clem?'

`No, this is his son speaking. Can I help you?'

Harald explained what the Center had been doing, then came to the heart of the matter.

`We're very grateful indeed for all the help your father has given us already. He's been more than generous. But the problem is, if we can't pay our fifteen-thousand-dollar mortgage in two days' time, the Center will have to fold.'

Harald eventually finished the call, not sure what was going to happen. Clem Stone and his son would have to talk the whole thing over. They had no right to expect anything from him. But at least he had let him know the true situation.

When the post arrived on September 10th, there was great excitement at the Center. Maybe, just maybe, it would contain a cheque big enough to save the Center. The staff tore open the envelopes, but to their great disappointment they contained only small donations from children. Still, they had to be thankful for anything.

They continued with their daily routine including their morning session in the chapel. The boys and girls were still thanking God in advance for the fifteen thousand dollars. David watched them with tears in his eyes. He admired their faith and their steadfastness. It would be such a pity if the Center had to close and they were back on the streets before they were ready. And what about the staff who had shown such dedication?

He felt a hand touch his shoulder gently.

`David, there's a delivery for you. You need to sign for it.'

The envelope had a Chicago postmark. It must be from Clem Stone. David's hand trembled as he hurried to open it. What if Mr Stone was writing to say that he couldn't help?

He pulled out a piece of paper. It was a certified cheque. For fifteen thousand dollars.

He went back into the chapel and stood at the front, with the piece of paper in his hand. He wanted to tell everybody what it was, but when he opened his mouth no words would come out. Instead he handed the cheque to Paul DiLena to pass round.

He watched the expressions on the young people's faces change as one by one they realized what it was. Their faces shone with delight, and tears of relief trickled down their faces onto the piece of paper. God had heard their prayers. Teen Challenge Center was safe.

CHAPTER TEN

`The Cross and
the Switchblade'

It was late and David was sitting at home, keeping his regular late night prayer appointment. The two hours after midnight that he spent in prayer had been an important feature of his life for a long time. He found that a lot of his best ideas came to him in these late night sessions. They seemed to put everything into perspective for him.

Tonight he found himself thinking about one of the favourite stories from the Old Testament. It was from the Second Book of Kings. In the story there is a great famine in Samaria because it has been besieged by King Ben-hadad of Syria. Four lepers outside the city gates decide to hand themselves over to the Syrians as they are likely to die of starvation anyway. But when they arrive at the army camp, they find to their astonishment that the Syrians have fled leaving all their possessions behind. They decide to go and share the good news with the Samaritans.

David had always thought it was a marvellous story, and it gave him pleasure to remember it. But time and time again throughout his prayer session the story kept coming back to him. It seemed to have some special significance.

After a few nights of thinking about the story, he eventually began to understand why it was important to him at this time in his life. He looked back over his time in New York, to the crusade at the Arena where Nicky and Israel and so many other boys and girls had found a new life.

He remembered how Teen-Age Evangelism had started and the number of young people who had been reached through the literature campaign and the television series.

And he thought about Teen Challenge Center, the wonderful young people he had working with him and the hundreds and thousands of young people who were getting to know God and finding new hope for their lives.

He was surrounded by the wealth of the Lord, just as the lepers in the story had been surrounded by rich booty. Shouldn't he share the marvellous news with others? But how could he do it so that enough people would hear it? He didn't know what he was meant to do, but he prayed that God would show him a way to spread the good news much more widely.

His prayer was answered when he eventually shared his feelings with Harald Bresden. Harald prayed for guidance on the spot, then straightaway offered a solution. He knew a couple of writers who worked on an inter-faith magazine called *Guideposts*. It might be a good idea for David to meet them.

The writers' names were John and Elizabeth Sherrill, but Elizabeth preferred to be called Tib. They suggested writing a three-part story about how David got involved with the kids in New York through his interest in the Farmer trial. After they had double-checked all the facts and persuaded the editor to run the story, it was eventually published in the magazine and caused a sensation. The American public loved it.

There was no doubt at all that people wanted to hear what God was doing in New York. The only question was what to do next. The idea of a book was mooted.

`How long do you reckon it would take if all three of us worked on it?' asked David cautiously. He was anxious that writing shouldn't interfere with his beloved work with the street kids. After all, that was what he was there for.

`To do it properly I think it would take about three years.'

David was taken aback. Three years. That was a huge time commitment. He wasn't sure if he really wanted to write a book, and if it was going to take up so much of his life he needed to know that it was God's will.

`I think we should put out a fleece,' said David. John and Tib didn't know what he was talking about but when he explained they agreed to go along with it. After all, working on the book would be a big commitment for them as well.

Together they decided upon some very tough criteria which would have to be satisfied as the conditions for the fleece. The Jewish publisher that John had in mind, Bernard Geis, should agree to see them immediately even though it was four o'clock on a Friday afternoon. He should agree to invest five thousand dollars and the basic agreement for the contract should be settled before they left his office.

John dialled the number and got through to Geis without any problem.

`Would it be possible for us to come and meet you this afternoon, Mr Geis?'

`Well, I have to leave the office in about an hour, but if you can come over straightaway I'm happy to see you.'

Condition number one had been fulfilled. David, John and Tib made a beeline for the office and introduced themselves to Mr Geis who was busy signing cheques.

`Would you tell me about the project you have in mind then?' he suggested.

`The Teen Challenge Center is doing some amazing work with the young people from the toughest areas of New York. If you'll allow me, I have some statistics that you might be interested in...'

Mr Geis didn't seem to be at all interested in

the figures which John rattled off for him. He carried on signing his cheques while John talked. It was obvious that his spiel wasn't having the desired effect.

After some time John realized that he was approaching the story in the wrong way. Statistics weren't very interesting to most people. But human beings were.

`Let me focus this a little differently. Think of it as a skinny preacher from the country who feels compelled to come to the big city to help some boys who're on a murder trial.'

Mr Geis sat up and listened, pushing his chequebook to one side. This was a story worth listening to. By five o'clock not only had he offered to publish the book, but he had also agreed to give them an advance of five thousand dollars.

Now clearly convinced that God wanted them to write the book, David, John and Tib settled down to the arduous task of researching the material for the book. For some of it the writers relied on David's own memories which he spoke into a tape-recorder for them. But there was other information they had to gather too, particularly from the young people who lived and worked at the Teen Challenge Center.

Then came draft after draft of material for the book. Tib and John wouldn't rest until they got it absolutely right, and prayed over each page, asking God to help them with bits they were finding particularly difficult. All in all, the book was entirely rewritten six times.

David wasn't allowed to read the early drafts, but when John and Tib felt they'd done as much as they could they handed the manuscript over to David and Gwen for their comments and alterations. The Christian couple's own lives took on a new dimension as they read about themselves and many a time they were moved to tears as they found themselves reliving particularly emotional events.

Soon the book was ready for publication. It was given the dramatic title *The Cross and the Switchblade*. It proved to be very successful and for several years it was one of the bestselling books in America. Even Hollywood film producers were impressed by it and several of them approached David wanting to buy the film rights.

Each time a film company showed an interest, David consulted John and Tib and asked them for their opinion. Like David, they had never made a film before, but they did give him one useful piece of advice. They knew that what mattered to David would be the integrity of the film. However, they thought it was unlikely that any of the producers would allow him to vet the script.

`Your best bet,' said Tib, `is to find yourself a producer and a lead actor that you can trust.'

David thought that was a sound idea and set

about praying for the right people to come along. Of course, they would have to be Christians so that they would really understand what the book was about.

Bernard Geis, David's publisher, wasn't so sure David was doing the right thing, as some of the offers that the pastor turned down were very lucrative. But in spite of that he respected David's wishes. They would wait until they received a suitable offer from someone who was a committed Christian.

One day Bernard Geis rang David to say that he thought someone had turned up trumps. The well-known singer Pat Boone wanted to buy the film rights for *The Cross and the Switchblade*.

`He should meet your requirements, David. After all, he's a Christian, isn't he?' Bernard was rather disappointed that David didn't sound as enthusiastic as he was about this particular offer.

`Can you arrange for Gwen and me to meet him?' asked David. He didn't want to commit himself until he knew a bit more about this singing star and his Christian faith.

Pat Boone met up with David and Gwen at an Italian restaurant in the centre of New York. He looked every inch a film star with his deep tan, white shoes and cowboy style clothes. But there was nothing flamboyant about his manner. He was friendly and natural and easy to get along with and they liked him very much.

`How did you find out about *The Cross and the Switchblade*?' asked David.

`I was working in Mexico City and it was on sale at the news-stand in the airport. I was going to use it as my bedtime reading, but once I started I couldn't put it down – even though I was supposed to be getting up at dawn.'

David smiled. It was always nice to know that his message was getting across to people.

`If I were to turn it into a movie, would you be willing to play your own part?' asked Pat.

David was taken aback. `I'm no actor,' he protested. `I belong out on the streets with kids who need help. I don't have the time to get involved with show business.'

`I take your point,' said Pat. `How do you feel about me producing it?'

David hesitated. He had heard Pat was a Christian but he wasn't sure how deep his faith really went. Would he have the spiritual maturity to do justice to the book?

`I don't know,' he said. `It's very important that we have the right producer – someone who understands what the book is all about. I'd be grateful if you could come along and talk to a few of the members of the Teen Challenge board.'

Pat agreed to do so, and a meeting was arranged at the Glad Tidings Tabernacle near Times Square. It was a dangerous area where lots of people were robbed and mugged. Still, reckoned David, it wouldn't do Pat any harm to see a bit of the darker side of New York life.

The meeting was not as informal as David might have liked. Pat, Gwen and David were seated side by side with their backs to the wall, while the other six people sat opposite them and fired questions at Pat about his beliefs and his lifestyle. David felt rather sorry for the poor man having to undergo such a fierce interrogation and ended up trying to put in a good word for him.

`Pat's well known for his clean living. It's a standard joke in Hollywood that he doesn't drink anything stronger than milk,' he argued, but he didn't feel he was cutting any ice with the board members.

The problem was that the board members really wanted to know if Pat was a born-again Christian who had experienced the Holy Spirit. But they didn't dare ask him outright. So they ended up talking in circles and never really coming to the point.

Eventually David took a firmer lead and explained what it was that they were looking for.

`I've got to explain something to you, Pat. The real reason for all this is that we won't make the movie unless we have committed Christians to produce it and to play the lead role.'

It sounded as if he was being terribly judgmental. After all, who was he to say whether Pat was a genuine Christian? He hoped he hadn't offended him.

Pat was generous enough to cope with it. He gave a big smile. `Well, all I can say is that I'm doing my best.'

David and his colleagues said goodbye to Pat and thanked him for coming. They had enjoyed meeting him. Now came the moment of truth when they discussed the man in his absence. Did they feel he really knew the Lord in the way they wanted?

The answer was no. But they bowed their heads and prayed that he would.

The movie rights remained unsold, and although several people made generous offers during the next three years, David still was no closer to finding the right person to produce the film version of *The Cross and the Switchblade* until he received a call from Dick Ross, a Christian producer who had worked on some films for Billy Graham. Over dinner with David and Gwen, Dick explained how he would approach the film.

`It's got to be an accurate portrayal of what happened, but I don't want lots of gratuitous sex and violence. It should be something that the whole family can watch together.'

David and Gwen were delighted. That was exactly what they wanted as well.

`And for the lead I'd like to use someone that you've already met, I believe. Pat Boone.'

David raised his eyebrows in surprise.

`By the way, Pat has a message for you. He wants you to know he has experienced the Holy Spirit.'

David smiled with relief. It looked as if his prayers had been answered.

`In that case, we seem to have the right team. I'll arrange for you to purchase the movie rights.' The fee was modest by Hollywood standards – ten thousand dollars, divided between the three co-authors, their agent, and Bernard Geis, the publisher.

David was overjoyed to find that the movie was going to be directed by Don Murray whom he knew to be a fine Christian. When the first draft of the script was ready, David and Gwen invited him over to their house to discuss it. But it just so happened that Nicky Cruz was in town, so David and Don went over to his hotel so that he could read it too.

They settled down with the manuscript, but David became more and more uncomfortable as he read on. This didn't sound like his story and the main character was nothing like him. But before saying anything about it, he asked Nicky for his opinion.

`Davie, this script would kill you.'

`I agree with you, Nicky. I'm very sorry, Don. It just isn't any good.'

`Never mind,' said Don. `We can change it as

much as you want. Let's see what we can do right now.'

Don spent all night and some of the next day going through the script page by page. He checked everything with David and Nicky and rewrote sections whenever he needed to.

There was just one speech that David didn't want to entrust to Don.

'The rally at the St Nicholas Arena is going to be the climax of the film, isn't it?' said the preacher. 'I'd like to rewrite the sermon myself.'

Don hesitated. It's one thing for a minister to write a sermon for a religious meeting, but writing for the big screen is a specialized skill that takes a long time to acquire.

'Go ahead,' said the director, looking rather anxious.

As he wrote, David was astonished how that night at the Arena came flooding back to him. It was as if he were back there again. He recalled every little detail, remembered words he had used, felt the fear and the elation that he had experienced. He channelled all that emotion into the script for the sermon.

When he had finished he felt happy with it. He felt as if God had been guiding him, but would Don be pleased with the result? He handed over the piece of paper and waited. While Don read the script the room was silent and time seemed to stand still.

'It's exactly right,' said Don. 'I won't need to change it at all.'

The arrangements for the production progressed steadily until Don was shooting the scenes with the actors. David went along to watch some of the filming but felt out of his depth most of the time. He didn't know very much about the complex business of film editing and found it difficult to imagine what the end result would be like as he was only seeing odd scenes shot out of sequence.

One thing he did enjoy was having a chance to speak to Pat Boone again. He wanted to know how Pat was now that God was really a part of his life. David turned up at the Reverend Ortez's church which the film company was using for the Arena scene. The original location at St Nicholas Arena had been demolished, so they had to use a substitute.

David was surprised by Pat's appearance. He no longer looked like a bronzed and healthy film star. In fact, he looked skinny and gaunt, rather like David himself. He had also been made up to look as much like him as possible and he was copying all his mannerisms. Pat was determined to give an accurate portrayal of David, and that included every little physical detail. It was unnerving to think that Pat was watching him so closely and storing everything he did in his memory.

David soon found out the reason why Pat

looked so gaunt. Pat's wife, Shirley, explained that she and Pat had both been fasting for three days. They both knew that the Arena scene was crucial to the whole movie, and they desperately wanted to make it work.

Before the filming, Pat himself was extremely nervous. He realized that God had been with David at the Arena and had given him the power to move the boys and girls who'd come along. Something very special had happened.

`I know I'm not the greatest actor in the world, David,' said Pat. `but I've got to make this convincing. Please, will you pray with me?'

David nodded. He understood how Pat felt. He laid his hands on the actor's shoulder and prayed for the Holy Spirit to be with them.

Everything was now ready. David went back to join Gwen and Shirley and waited for the action. Soon the cameras were turning and Pat was preaching the sermon that David had written, re-creating what had happened the night when Nicky had been converted. And it was as fresh and as powerful as it had been all those years ago. David forgot he was watching an actor. Pat was like a real preacher.

Something happened during one of the breaks that convinced David the power of the episode would really come across to people who saw the film. One of the younger actors came over and spoke to David. He told him that he hadn't been a Christian when he accepted a part in *The Cross and the Switchblade* and he'd looked upon it as just another job. But he'd been so moved by what he'd experienced on the film-set that now he wanted to give his life to God.

`Please, will you pray for me?' he asked.

He had tears in his eyes and David felt a lump in his own throat as well. This was exactly what he had been hoping for. *The Cross and the Switchblade* wasn't just another movie. It was something that would change people's lives.

*　　*　　*　　*　　*　　*

The film version of *The Cross and the Switchblade* was a great success. Throughout the country it played to packed cinemas, and David heard again and again that people had become Christians after seeing it. But did this mean that Teen Challenge would be able to say goodbye to all its money worries when the royalties started to come in?

David certainly hoped so. It would be a big relief if they didn't have to pray for money all the time. It would give them more time to pray for people in need.

Gwen, however, was sceptical. She didn't believe it was God's will for them to have so much money because that would mean they wouldn't need to depend on Him every day for their needs.

She was right. First of all, the royalty cheques were late in arriving from Hollywood; then

David received a phone call from the producer, Dick Ross. He explained that there had been a lot of expenses that they hadn't bargained for, so the royalties might be delayed.

Just a few days later, an attorney rang up and said he was acting for Bernard Geis Associates, the company which had published the book. It had gone bankrupt. David was devastated. To this day he finds it hard to believe that the book which sold over fifteen million copies in dozens of languages could have been a financial failure for its publisher.

But at the time he thought only about how it would affect him and Teen Challenge. And the more he thought about it, the angrier he became. At first he thought his anger was justified. After all, he'd arranged for all the royalties from both the book and the film to go towards the work of Teen Challenge. It was the kids on the streets who would be losing out, not him personally.

`I'll sue the company,' he resolved. `I'm not going to let them get away with it.'

But as soon as he started to investigate the practicalities of taking out a lawsuit, he changed his mind. It would be an extremely expensive business. He would need fifteen thousand dollars just to set it going, and the costs could eventually rise much higher.

But there were other considerations too. Suing his publisher would not be fitting for a Christian. The Bible said that Christians shouldn't go to court with other believers. And David believed that he and his colleagues at Teen Challenge were called upon to be good stewards, not money-grubbers.

In monetary terms the film fared no better than the book. It got good reviews from the critics and its box office takings amounted to more than six million dollars even before the television rights had been sold. But in spite of its success, the producer lost money on it, and it did not provide the financial security for Teen Challenge that everyone had been hoping for.

So the staff and residents of Teen Challenge were not to stop praying for their daily bread. They still had to depend on God to provide the money they needed for all of their bills. If anything, the success of the film and the book made it harder for them to raise funds. Many of the people who had supported them stopped doing so because they mistakenly believed that the Center now had more than enough money for all its needs.

In a way they were back to square one. Yet David believed that the book and the film had served their real purpose. If God could reach people through them, that was all that mattered. And maybe it wasn't such a bad thing that they hadn't made much money out of the film or the book. If it kept them close to God and dependent on him, it could really turn out to be a blessing in disguise.

CHAPTER ELEVEN

——

`My brother was lost'

One Sunday morning the telephone rang. It was Jerry, David's younger brother, phoning from Manhattan.

`I want to see you David. How do I get to your house from here?'

It was a relief that Jerry had finally called. David had been praying for him ever since the previous night when Mother told him about Jerry's threat to kill himself. Jerry must be terribly unhappy, but David believed he might be able to help him, if only he'd show up.

Out of the three brothers in the family, Jerry, David and Don, Jerry had always been the difficult one. Even as a child, Jerry was nothing like David, in looks or in personality. He felt stifled by the religious upbringing he'd been given and all the time he was growing up he had constant battles with his father over discipline.

As a teenager, he came to resent David as well. The two boys just didn't see eye to eye. David wished that Jerry would act in a more responsible manner, and Jerry wished that his goody-goody brother would stop putting him down.

But then Jerry grew up and got a job in Pittsburg as a supermarket manager. He married a lovely girl called Evelyn and had four children of his own. By the time David was running Teen Challenge, he and Jerry didn't have much contact with one another, but he didn't worry too much about that. Jerry seemed to be getting on with his life quite well without any help from him.

At least that was what David thought until one day he heard that Jerry was fast becoming an alcoholic. And over the next few years, alcohol became a bigger and bigger part of Jerry's life. He began to skip his work to go drinking with his friends and eventually he walked out on his wife and children.

But now Jerry was desperate. Desperate enough to swallow his pride and come and ask his brother for help. Maybe that meant he was ready to change. David certainly hoped so.

David went to pick him up from the ferry and was horrified to see how ill and unkempt Jerry now looked. He hadn't shaved and he had aged a lot since the last time they'd been together.

Once Jerry had showered and shaved, David sat down with him and tried to find out why he was so distressed. The answer that he got from Jerry made him feel extremely uncomfortable. Apparently, one of the shops where Jerry had worked sold books, including *The Cross and the Switchblade* and the other assistants were always asking him if he was related to David Wilkerson. He said it emphasized the fact that his own brother hardly ever made the effort to spend any time with him.

`I was always seeing you on TV,' said Jerry. `There you were, talking about how you were saving all these people. But I knew it didn't matter to you whether I lived or died.'

That criticism hit David hard. His concern for Jerry turned to guilt for not having given him more support over the years. How could he have been so busy with his own affairs that he forgot about his own brother?

Jerry also had some practical problems. He had run up a lot of debts as a result of his drinking. Together they amounted to three hundred dollars. There was no way he could pay them off himself.

David was determined to do everything he could to give Jerry a fresh start, so he flew with him to Pittsburg and settled all the accounts that he had with various shops and businesses. He then found him somewhere else to stay and introduced him to an Assemblies of God church where the pastor seemed supportive. If Jerry had someone to go to when things got rough, he might be able to stay on the straight and narrow.

Then there was the question of his brother's job which he had lost because of his heavy drinking. David went with Jerry to the supermarket and was delighted when the management agreed to give him another chance.

It looked as if Jerry's life was back on an even

keel once more, thanks to David's help. At the time, Jerry seemed grateful and for once the antagonism between the brothers seemed to have disappeared.

`You're all right, David,' said Jerry, as the two men said goodbye to one another.

`So are you, Jerry. Just remember that it's up to you what happens from now on. You can either get on with your life or you can go out and get drunk again.'

Unfortunately, Jerry chose to continue with his drinking. In no time at all he was back on the bottle, and he left his new lodgings without giving a forwarding address. The pastor of the church didn't know where he was either. He had only gone there once.

With no way of contacting Jerry, all David could do now was pray for him. He and Gwen remembered him in their prayers every day and so did everyone at Teen Challenge. But it was Jerry's mother who showed the greatest commitment to him. She prayed for him constantly. She would never ever give up on her son. One day he would get back in touch she insisted.

She was right. Some time later, he turned up out of the blue at Teen Challenge and asked if he could take part in the rehabilitation programme for alcoholics.

`I really want to beat my drink problem this time, David. It's ruined my life.'

Overjoyed to see him again, David admitted him to the Teen Challenge Center. There he would receive all the help he needed to overcome his addiction. It looked as if this time Jerry might be on the way to recovery.

But Jerry only stayed at the Center for two weeks. Then off he went on his own yet again, back to his old ways. David heard he was living like a down-and-out in the Bowery, an area of Manhattan where many drunks hung out. He tried walking the streets, hoping he would see his brother, but he never did.

Jerry appeared to have reached rock bottom. It was hardly possible for him to sink any lower. But all David and his family could do was pray even more fervently that Jerry might return and find a solution to his problems.

Some time later David invited Pat Boone to come and conduct a crusade with him at Glad Tidings, Pastor Berg's church. Pat was in New York anyway doing some filming.

`I'd love to be involved,' said Pat. `Only I'd rather you didn't advertise it. You could be swamped with people who were only coming to see me and didn't want to hear about the Lord. I think it would be better if you spread the news by word of mouth.'

`Of course,' said David. But somehow he forgot to pass the message on to the pastor of the church who placed a modest advertisement in one of the newspapers.

When he found out about the mistake, David
was a little bit annoyed with himself. But he
didn't know how that advertisement would
change his life. For one of the people who read it
was Jerry.

The day of the crusade arrived and Pat and
David and their wives were preparing to enter
the packed auditorium when the director of the
crusade came over with a message for David.

`David, there's something I think you should
know. Jerry's here.'

`How is he?'

`He looks terrible.'

David didn't know why his brother had come,
but he was pleased that he had. It meant that
God hadn't deserted Jerry after all. He began to
hope that tonight would be a turning point for
all the guests at the rally, and especially for Jerry.

The meeting began and Pat gave his
testimony as planned. All through the
proceedings David was thinking about Jerry,
praying for Jerry, wondering what he was
making of the meeting so far. Eventually it was
time for David to stand up and speak, and from
his new position he could see where Jerry was
sitting.

David's heart began to beat faster. He had
decided he was going to do something unprece-
dented, something that could be very risky
indeed. He was going to appeal directly to Jerry

in front of a church full of people to give his life
to God.

If it worked, there was a chance that Jerry
might be saved. But on the other hand, such a
challenge could make Jerry run off again and
ruin David's credibility with the other people
who had come along to the crusade.

`Ladies and gentlemen,' said David. `I'm
going to do something that I've never done
before, but please bear with me. I have something to say to one particular person who's here
tonight. I don't know how he'll respond to what
I say, but I hope he'll come out here and make
his peace with the Lord.'

He looked towards where his brother was
sitting. `Jerry, tonight I'm asking you in the
name of the Lord to come back and take His
side. Come and give your life to Jesus.'

A hush fell upon the congregation as everyone
waited to see what Jerry would do. David stood
quite still, his hand extended in welcome, and
prayed silently for his brother.

Jerry stood up. He looked like an old man and
his clothes were dirty and tattered. He didn't say
anything, but he pushed past the person next to
him to reach the aisle. He hesitated there as if he
wasn't sure whether to go forward or go out.

But suddenly he made his choice. He rushed
to the front of the church and knelt in front of his
astonished brother.

`Save me, Lord Jesus,' he cried. `Save me, I'm a terrible sinner.'

David's eyes filled with tears and he couldn't speak for the big lump that was in his throat. But Pat Boone got onto his knees beside Jerry and led him in a prayer of commitment, getting Jerry to repeat it after him, line by line.

By now the whole church was in tears, including Jerry himself. They were tears of joy. Jerry had finally found his way back to the Lord.

Later, when David discussed Jerry's future with him, they decided together that it would be best if he went to the Teen Challenge rehabilitation farm in Pennsylvania to overcome his alcohol problem. This time he threw himself into his recovery programme wholeheartedly. He really wanted to be cured.

Jerry was growing as a Christian as well as he studied his Bible far into the night. And instead of griping about his problems as he used to, he now counted his blessings and gave thanks to God for everything he had.

About six months after the crusade, Jerry went to his old town, Pittsburg, on a Teen Challenge outing. There he took another huge step forward by making a phone call to his wife, Evelyn. He would like to see her and the children again. Would it be possible for him to pay them a visit?

She said that it would. Jerry went along to the house where they lived feeling rather nervous, but his family gave him a warm welcome. It was amazing to see them all again after such a long time. If only he could go back and live with them! Fortunately they were thinking the same thing, so Jerry soon moved back into the family home. All he needed now was a job.

Before long, that particular need was taken care of too. One of the directors of Teen Challenge was looking for a travelling representative. He telephoned Jerry and offered him the post. Jerry jumped at the chance. From the start he loved his new job, and particularly enjoyed sharing with alcoholics his experience of how God had transformed his life.

David was overjoyed at how things had worked out this time for Jerry. Time was proving that his conversion wasn't any five minute wonder. Now Jerry really had found his way back to the Lord. And David could rest in the knowledge that, at long last, his brother was safe and happy.

CHAPTER TWELVE

Going astray

Even the greatest of men are only human beings, and we all have moments when our short-comings become all too apparent. David is no exception.

Although the film and the book of *The Cross and the Switchblade* were not a financial success for David, they did, however, make a big difference to his life. Before the publication of the book, both David and Teen Challenge were largely unknown. David and colleagues worked in a very simple way, finding their own solutions to the problems that confronted them day by day. They stayed close to God. They had to, as they relied on Him to meet their every need.

But after the publication of *The Cross and the Switchblade*, things changed. David assumed a new status in the eyes of the public. Suddenly people perceived him as an expert on drug rehabilitation, and like many experts he was in great demand from the press and other media. Several of the top newspapers and magazines in the United States ran features on Teen Challenge, and David received more invitations than he could handle to speak at various events and meetings.

No longer was Teen Challenge a simple organization without any frills or pretensions. Extra telephone lines and a clutch of secretaries were now needed to deal with the myriad calls and letters that flooded the office every day.

The skinny preacher was no longer a nobody from the country. He had become public property, a national figure. Just walking along the street, he would be recognized. People would come up and speak to him as he was going about his daily business. `Mr Wilkerson, what do you think of such and such?' `Mr Wilkerson, I'm worried about my son – what do you think the problem is?'

These sorts of pressures began to affect the rest of his family as well. To protect their privacy, for the first time in his life David now had to use an ex-directory telephone number. Otherwise the family would never have been able to have a meal together in peace or make time for themselves to relax and forget about work.

All this attention was a nuisance, but it was also flattering in a way. He may not have thought about it on a conscious level, but deep down David was beginning to think of himself as an important person. After all, he was heavily in demand. He had to appear on television and radio, be interviewed, make guest appearances at meetings. And when he spoke, people took notice of what he said.

The preacher was jolted out of his complacency by an unexpected meeting which took place in the summer of 1968. He was dashing along Clinton Avenue from the original headquarters at number 416 to the organization's new building at number 444, when he encountered a Chinaman. The Chinaman was right in front of him on the pavement. David nearly knocked him over in his haste to get on.

Someone was going to have to move. David took a step to the left, but so did the Chinaman. Then he took a step to the right, but the Chinaman followed suit. Yet another, and still there was no way to get round the Chinaman, who appeared to be blocking his way on purpose.

The mysterious gentleman stared David in the eye. `David Wilkerson,' he said in impeccable English. `The Lord has sent me from Hong Kong to give you a message.'

David was startled. He had been accosted by a divine messenger from half-way round the world! What sort of message could he possibly have to give him? While he was still speculating, the Chinaman spelt his message out in no uncertain terms.

`You have lost your simplicity,' he said. `You are not depending on God any more. You are depending on David Wilkerson.'

David tried to reply without being too rude, but underneath he was seething. He thought the

Chinaman had no right to speak to him like that. After all, he was an important person, a person who could influence the whole country. How dare this stranger stop him in the middle of the street and make such a terrible accusation.

Something in David's manner must have betrayed his displeasure, for a tear moistened the Chinaman's cheek.

`I didn't want to upset you, David. I know the Lord has done many great things through you. But I had to do what He told me. I had no choice.'

Later that day David recounted his strange experience to Gwen, hoping that she would reassure him that it had all been a big mistake. The Chinaman must have been raving. `You don't believe him, do you?' he asked his wife. `You don't really think I've lost my simplicity?'

`It's something you need to think about,' replied Gwen.

Because Gwen hadn't pooh-poohed the Chinaman's message, David was beginning to take it seriously. He respected Gwen's judgement. She was often very perceptive when it came to spiritual matters. Maybe he had changed and everybody knew except him?

But what did the Chinaman mean when he said he had lost his simplicity? Was he talking about material comforts? David remembered his early days in New York when he was camping out in the Teen Challenge office, cooking all his food on a little stove. He used to pray for hours, for there was nothing to distract him there. Life was simple then all right.

But once Gwen and the children had joined him in the city, he couldn't expect them to adopt such a primitive lifestyle, could he? True, they did have a comfortable house now and a nice car. But their way of life wasn't any grander now than it had been back in Philipsburg. So what was the Chinaman talking about when he said `You have lost your simplicity.'?

David needed time to think, so the following day he cancelled all his appointments and set off on his own in his car to revisit the Trysting Places where he had often met with God in the past. Maybe he would find the answer at one of those.

First of all, he went to the place where he had been brought up as a child, Barnesboro in Pennsylvania. But today that didn't bring him any inspiration, so he drove instead to Old Baldy Hill with its views of Barnesboro and the road which led out of town. But he didn't feel drawn to spending any time there either.

Philipsburg was next on his list of destinations. It was years since he left his parish to go and live in New York and he wondered whether it would have changed.

It hadn't. It was still a down-to-earth country town. As he drove through it, memories came flooding back to him of parishioners that he had known, conversations he had had, happy times that he and his family had shared with this simple little community.

But he still hadn't found what he was looking for, a Trysting Place. Then suddenly he remembered somewhere else! Albert Hill! How many times had he sat up there looking out over Philipsburg and the church and his own back garden?

He perched on his favourite rock and looked through his favourite copy of the Bible which he had brought with him. It was the same one he had held up for the photographers to see when he had been thrown out of the Michael Farmer trial, the one that had been in all the newspapers. The margins were full of notes he had made through the years. They charted his own spiritual journey with all its moments of agony and ecstasy.

He read text after text, then suddenly he understood the simplicity the Chinaman had been talking about. It was a simplicity of faith. It was the sort of faith he had shown when he first made his journeys to New York and started working with the boys from the streets. Complete and utter dependence upon God.

There on the hill, he bowed his head and prayed, greatly relieved that the meaning of the Lord's message had finally got through to him.

`Thank you, Lord, for showing me where I was going wrong. From now on, let me rely upon You, instead of relying on David Wilkerson.'

* * * * * *

Another area of his life in which David made some mistakes was his marriage. He had always considered himself a very lucky man because Gwen was everything he could have wished for in a wife. She was supportive and calm and never nagged, and he could always count on her for wise advice. She was a devoted Christian with a very deep understanding of life and faith. So it never occurred to him that one day he might seriously think of leaving her, especially at a time when she was vulnerable and in need of his support. But that was exactly what happened.

The difficulties began when his wife was struck by illness. At that time she was still quite young, which made the situation even harder to bear. Serious illnesses are things that happen to old people, not to people with small children – or at least that's what Gwen and David thought.

At first there didn't seem to be much wrong with Gwen. She had discovered a lump on her side, so the couple went to get their own doctor to check it out. He told them it was just a swollen ovary and no cause for concern.

But when Gwen began to experience excruciating pains, David began to think there was something more sinister wrong with her. Gwen had never been one to make a fuss about illness, and at first she used to just grit her teeth and pretend there was nothing wrong. But eventually, on a trip to visit her mother in Pittsburg, the pain became so bad that she couldn't pretend any longer.

David took Gwen to see a Pittsburg specialist who examined her carefully, then had a private word with David. He advised him to get Gwen to hospital in New York as soon as possible.

Now David was in a difficult position. He didn't want to alarm Gwen, so he persuaded her to go back to New York, but didn't tell her how serious her illness was. Gwen for her part played along with him and made out that she was only going for a rest.

Then came the bombshell. Their family doctor rang David to tell him the result of tests that had been done at the Staten Island General Hospital. Gwen had cancer. The doctor's initial diagnosis of a swollen ovary had been a mistake. She would need an operation straightaway.

David couldn't bear to tell her. He tried to make out that she was going into hospital for some tests. There was no way he could face up to the awful truth of his wife's illness. It was terrifying. Even when Gwen was being wheeled into the theatre for an exploratory operation, David still couldn't be honest with her. He couldn't face it, couldn't bear to tell her it was cancer.

Finally, David was shocked to his senses by the news that Gwen had a large growth at the junction of her bowel.

`I'm not walking in the Light,' he told himself. `I'm not being honest with Gwen.'

Fortunately, the Wilkersons' family doctor happened to be at the hospital. David asked him to come and help him explain to Gwen what was happening to her. The doctor was glad. He felt that Gwen would cope with her illness better if she knew exactly what it was she was up against.

Being honest with Gwen was a turning point. When the couple were finally alone, Gwen broke down and cried. At last they were communicating instead of just playing games with one another.

To David's surprise, he discovered that Gwen had known all along that she was suffering from cancer. She had been trying to spare his feelings. Even now, she was trying to give him strength by telling him about a promise she'd had from God.

She said that God had promised to give them both the faith of Shadrach to help them through their ordeal. The faith that Shadrach, Meshach and Abednego had, according to the Book of Daniel, when Nebuchadnezzar cast them into the burning fiery furnace. Together Gwen and David prayed for faith to cope with their ordeal.

Gwen's cancer turned out to be even more

extensive than the doctors had envisaged, but they removed all they could find. Eventually Gwen was sent home to recover from her operation. She and David made sure that they talked to each other this time.

More than a year elapsed, then Gwen had another scare. She began to feel unwell again, as if a growth was sapping all the strength from her body. This time they didn't take any chances. Gwen went to see the consultant straightaway.

Fortunately, this time it really was a non-malignant lump. But the realization that the cancer might come back had given Gwen a serious scare. She had even begun to wonder whether she might be better off dying now rather than having to cope with her fear of the cancer recurring.

There was one good thing that came out of this scare, though. Painfully aware of her own mortality, Gwen decided that she wanted to have another baby. She thought it would help her to feel that her life hadn't come to an end. David was concerned that a pregnancy might be too much for Gwen's body to cope with after two recent operations. However, their doctor gave them the all-clear, and a year later Gwen gave birth to a son, Greg, who was her pride and joy.

Greg was only a year old when Gwen became sick again. On a trip to Memphis, Tennessee, Gwen found herself in great pain. She had been passing blood as well. David tried to get her back home, but she was so ill that they had to stop off and see a doctor in Pennsylvania. All he could do was give her some painkillers and recommend that she should get back to New York as soon as possible.

`I'm afraid the news is bad,' announced the consultant. `You're going to need a hysterectomy, Mrs Wilkerson. I'm sorry, but there's really no alternative.'

It was a major operation, and it turned out to have huge effects on the couple's life together. The doctor had tried to warn David that Gwen might undergo mood swings and depression after the operation. They were normal emotional reactions to the physical changes that she was undergoing.

`Yes, Doctor. I understand,' said David. `I'll make allowances for her.' He was quite convinced that he would manage to deal with any problems that Gwen might experience. After all, they'd beaten cancer before. Surely they could do it again. But he had underestimated just how great a toll his wife's irrational behaviour would have on him and his ability to cope.

David couldn't believe how deeply depressed Gwen had become. She didn't want to pray or read the Bible any more and she would burst into tears if he tried to talk to her about her problems. She didn't want anything to do with other people and she had started to shout at the children, something that she had never done before.

David took refuge in prayer, adding an extra hour to his nightly two-hour prayer time. But going to bed at three in the morning began to wear him out and make him impatient with her. He found himself getting angry with his wife, even though her unreasonable behaviour was only what the doctor had predicted.

The preacher was tired of the fiery ordeal they were undergoing. Tired of dealing with Gwen and having to be strong for both of them.

And then something happened which took him completely by surprise. Gwen repeatedly accused him of having affairs with teenagers. Of course, this sort of jealousy was all tied up with her hysterectomy and was part and parcel of the emotional problems that the consultant had warned him about.

All the same, David was deeply distressed that his own wife could think him capable of such a thing. And it didn't matter how much he tried to reassure her, she wouldn't believe him. She was convinced he didn't love her and wanted to get away from her.

To his horror, the idea of leaving Gwen started to seem attractive to him. Why should he carry on battling all the time? It wasn't doing Gwen any good. Who knows? Perhaps she might even be happier without him?

Soon David was fantasizing about getting some money out of the bank and going off to Mexico on his own. It became his escape valve. He would try really hard for a spell to stick with Gwen and help her, then eventually he would have a period where all he thought about was leaving her.

The crisis point came at a banquet and rally which David and Gwen were attending on the West Coast. He had hoped that the trip might do Gwen good. But before the banquet they had another of their terrible rows. He just couldn't get through to Gwen at all.

The banquet was an embarrassing endurance test, with David trying to be polite and Gwen sulking all through dinner.

Something in David snapped. He had had enough.

Why should he stay and suffer like this? Life with Gwen was intolerable. It was all a terrible effort, and for nothing, he thought.

Because he was due to go on a foreign trip very soon, David had his passport and a lot of travellers' cheques with him. So what was there to stop him? He could leave straightaway and be in Mexico that night.

He got up from his seat and excused himself. Gwen didn't even look at him. He left the hotel and walked towards the bus station, all the time imagining what he would do once he got to

Mexico. According to the timetable, a bus would be leaving soon for Mexico City, taking him to his new life.

Then he heard a voice ringing out. `David, you're a fool,' it said. He knew it was God speaking to him, but He sounded kindly and compassionate rather than judgmental. Suddenly David was alert and eager to hear more.

`You know you have to persevere, David. It's Gwen who's been ill, not you. I know you're tired, but don't give in, my son. Come to Me.'

David knew what he had to do. He ran all the way back to the hotel, into the room where the banquet was being held. The organizers looked relieved to see him and even Gwen smiled.

`I love you, Gwen,' he whispered, kissing his wife on the cheek. He knew that he would never give up loving her, no matter how difficult that might be, because God's love for him would never fail. Not even in his darkest moments.

Two weeks later Gwen and David set off together on a second honeymoon during which they managed to recapture their love for one another. At last they were happy together again. But they didn't let that blind them to the fact that they would have to work at their marriage again and again. They developed some guidelines to help them through sticky patches in their relationship.

Life was never going to be without problems,

and some of the difficulties they would have to face together would test them even more sorely. Only now they had learned to face up to them together, and to realize that God would be with them, no matter how great their pain and despair.

CHAPTER THIRTEEN

Kids' Town

David was trying his best to keep his faith
simple, bearing in mind the Chinaman's
warning. And his marriage was much happier
now that he and Gwen were communicating
with each other again. But along with new
challenges, his work also brought him new
temptations. The problem was knowing which
was which.

He was convinced that the work that Teen
Challenge did was invaluable. It helped a lot of
people who were in desperate need, so it was
surely a good idea to expand it as much as
possible. The organization had, in fact, grown
quite considerably. It had started off with just
one building on Clinton Avenue, but now had
five; and in addition there were now four
rehabilitation farms in various parts of North
America.

The work of Teen Challenge was also being
carried out at forty-six centres throughout the
United States and Canada. These were run by
local churches, and were independent of David's
organization, although they adopted similar
principles. The founder of the Dallas-Fort Worth
Teen Challenge, Howard Foltz, had also set up
fifty centres all over Europe.

Yes, Teen Challenge was definitely a success story, and the bigger the success, the greater David's prestige. It was hard to keep a sense of perspective when life was a whirlwind of activity and so many people seemed to be depending on him, looking to him for advice.

Occasionally in one of his off-guard moments, David sensed that his frenetic lifestyle might not be exactly what God wanted of him. But then he would get caught up in a morass of appointments and demands on his time and he would forget to ask himself why he was doing all this.

David was for ever dreaming of new projects. That was one of his great strengths – the fact that he was a man who had dreams and followed them come what may. Without his dreams he would never have come to New York, never set up Teen Challenge. But sometimes they could be dangerous as well. He'd get carried away with them and the distinction between God's will and his own will would become blurred.

One such dream was Kids' Town. It was a dream on a grand scale to construct a whole town right next to Disney World in Florida where troubled boys and girls could come and live. It would occupy one hundred and fifty acres and cost over eight million dollars to build. The very thought of raising such a huge sum of money made him tingle with excitement.

Had he asked the Lord for guidance, he might have realized that he was the one who wanted

Kids' Town, not God, but he was so attached to the project that he couldn't even pray about it. It was a great idea. It was obvious that Kids' Town would be terrific.

So David forged ahead with his plans. Teen Challenge took out an option on the land and preliminary plans for the development were drawn up at a cost of five thousand dollars.

Spending money on such a scale, it was obvious that David had forgotten the day when they had prayed so hard for just thirty-two dollars for food for the day. Or perhaps he thought it proved how far he had come. A skinny guy from the country working on a multimillion dollar project – that was a turn-up for the books!

David was intent on making Kids' Town a reality and he continued making plans and raising funds – until one evening he was stopped in his tracks. He was in Chicago where he had arranged to make a presentation to ten thousand people about the Kids' Town project.

But sitting on the platform, waiting for his turn to speak, he suddenly felt sick in the pit of his stomach. He had a moment of clarity and he could see what he'd really been doing and who he'd been doing it for.

'Look at yourself, David. Look at what you've turned into. A glorified PR man. Is that what the Lord called you to be?'

The Lord Himself answered that question for him.

`Raising funds is not what I called you for.'

`But what about the thousands of young people who could benefit from Kids' Town, Lord? Youngsters who have known so little happiness in their lives? How can I deprive them of such a marvellous experience?'

Again, David heard the Lord's voice. `You can't put everyone into an institution, David.'

It was true. He knew it was. It didn't matter how many youngsters he could offer help to through Kids' Town. There would always be others crying out for help, far more than he could ever deal with. It was a sad fact of life.

David didn't speak about Kids' Town at the meeting that night. Instead he preached a simple sermon about finding peace. A sermon to himself.

In his own prayer-room back home David settled down for his late-night prayer session. He wanted to get his relationship with God back on a proper footing. To find God's peace in his life. And he was determined to stay there until he did.

He prayed that he might feel Jesus' presence, and he did. He felt a wave of peace sweep over him, and immediately relaxed. Then he prayed for some answers to the things that had been worrying him. Why had he gone his own way and ignored God's will? And how could he prevent it from happening again?

That night he found a new understanding of

the purpose of his life and ministry. He now believed he was called to a ministry where he would be working with people. Other people might be called upon to develop institutions, but that wasn't his particular calling and he needed to recognize that.

He also learned how much he needed to follow God's guidance day by day and seek specific advice about what he was to do. Only that way could he make sure that he was carrying out the will of God rather than following his own inclinations.

There in his prayer-room, David asked the Lord's opinion on each of the projects that he was involved in. Did the Lord want him to continue with them?

The biggest project was, of course, Kids' Town. When he asked the Lord if he was to carry on with it, he got a very clear answer. `No.'

David hesitated. It was difficult to give up his pet project when he had spent such a lot of time and energy developing it already, not to mention the five thousand dollars that had already been devoted to the preliminary work. Was it right to waste so much money?

But still the same answer came back. The Lord did not want him to go ahead with Kids' Town. And if some money had been wasted, that was part of what it cost for David to learn his lesson.

`I'll tell you what your real motivation was for Kids' Town, David,' said the Lord. `It wasn't for

Me or for the young people. It was to be a monument to yourself.'

It was true, and David recognized it. He had fallen into a trap, and he never wanted to make the same mistake again.

David felt much happier when he woke up the next day. It was as if a great weight had been lifted from him. No longer did he have to struggle with demands and deadlines and drudgery. All he had to do was pray about each of his commitments and God would let him know what he really needed to do. No longer would he be a slave to his schedules.

He broke the news to the family that Kids' Town wasn't going to happen. He was surprised at how well they took it. Gwen wasn't at all disappointed, and all Greg thought of was how glad he was that Daddy didn't have to go on the trip to Florida that he'd been planning. He ran next door to tell his little friend that Daddy would be staying at home after all.

David's next task was to tell the Teen Challenge staff that he was calling off the Kids' Town project and explain to them why he had changed his mind. Again, he was delighted with their reaction. They were relieved to hear the news. It seemed that if David would only follow the Lord's guidance, life would be simpler and happier for everyone.

The purge didn't stop with Kids' Town. David asked the Lord about all the other engagements he had in his diary. Several times he was told to cancel them.

David's first reaction was to feel guilty about letting people down and spoiling their plans. But as he obeyed God's instructions, he began to see that it would do him good to prune some of the appointments from his schedule.

But the next thing the Lord suggested was more radical. He wanted David to take a year's sabbatical.

`But how will everyone manage without me?'

`That's your whole problem, David. You don't believe that they'll manage. But they will.'

Relieved of the straitjacket he had created for himself, David experienced a new lease of life. He didn't have to be constantly on the go just to convince himself that he was wanted. He could go out onto the streets and speak to young people; he could preach when he felt called to preach.

Both mentally and physically, he began to feel the benefits of his new way of life. Nowadays he felt fresh after a day's work, instead of exhausted. He could go out into the fresh air and play games with the children. And he even looked younger.

He didn't have to struggle any longer. And it was wonderful!

Through his new flexible approach he also discovered new methods of working. No longer did he feel he had to bring every addict to Teen

Challenge and enrol him in the rehabilitation programme. Instead he asked the Lord about each person, and brought back only a few, entrusting the others to the care of the local churches.

Gradually, the Lord allowed him to do a little more work with groups. Still consulting the Lord about every invitation, David occasionally received permission to accept one or two. And that was how he found himself facing another new challenge in his ministry.

He had been in Chicago visiting an old friend and supporter of his, Al. Just before David left, Al confided in him that he and his wife had been having problems with their fifteen–year–old son, Jimmy. He didn't think it was anything serious, but the boy didn't seem to have been quite his usual self recently.

`I wonder if you could have a word with him, David. You get on well with teenagers. Maybe you could find out what the problem is?'

David went upstairs to Jimmy's room, which was comfortably furnished and full of the various pieces of hi-fi and sports equipment that middle–class kids like to have. It was a far cry from the sort of room where youngsters like Nicky and Israel would have slept when they were Jimmy's age.

Yet one thing was all too familiar to David. The reek of marijuana.

The tall blond teenager whom David encountered was far from happy. As soon as he saw David he was on the defensive.

`This was Dad's idea, wasn't it?'

`He just wants you to talk to me. Maybe you don't feel you can talk to him.'

`It's his fault. He never listens,' retorted Jimmy.

But gradually, as Jimmy began to trust David, he dropped his guard and opened up. David was shocked at what he heard. Jimmy had started drinking when he was only thirteen years old, but by the following year he had graduated to drugs, which he preferred because they didn't make him vomit.

The drugs he liked best were more sophisticated than the ones the street kids used. Jimmy took amphetamines to give him a high in the morning and barbiturates to calm him down at night. His friends were also keen on LSD, a drug which induced hallucinations and a false sense of reality.

David was horrified by what he heard. He could understand why some of the kids in the slums took drugs. Their lives were so hopeless that drugs provided a way (albeit transitory) for them to escape from their desperate situation for a while. But for a kid like Jimmy from a good home to have fallen under the control of drugs and drink at such a young age – that was unthinkable! What on earth was he going to say to Al?

He tried to break the news gently in the car on the way to the airport, but Al took it very badly. He refused to believe the things David told him about Jimmy and attributed them all to David's overactive imagination. He'd been working with the dregs of society so long that now he was finding fault with decent kids as well.

David had lost a friend, which hurt him a lot. But worse than that – he had discovered there were kids out in the comfortable suburbs who needed help just as badly as the ones on the streets of New York.

Now that he was aware of the problem, it loomed large everywhere he turned. He couldn't even go to a youth rally without seeing middle class youngsters who were obviously high on drugs.

He tried to get to know them and find out what they did, why they did it. They didn't mind talking to him over coffee after the meetings. Through these conversations it emerged that what he, an expert on addiction, knew about drugs was only the tip of the iceberg.

These suburban young people had access to a wide range of chemical and artificially produced drugs, for which they used fanciful nicknames such as `Christmas trees', `footballs' and `blue jackets'. But the Mafia were also introducing heroin into their areas, knowing that these young people were a ready market with plenty of money to spend.

David began to tell other adults – parents, teachers, ministers – about the problems he was uncovering in the suburbs. But nobody wanted to know. Like Al, they simply didn't believe him – or maybe they were too frightened to admit that they did. They associated drugs with inner-city life, not suburbia. Things like that didn't happen in the areas where they lived, among responsible, well-to-do people.

It was in 1964 that David became aware of the drug problem in the suburbs, but it wasn't until 1967 that the first middle-class drug addict turned up at David's Teen Challenge Center. He was a well-educated young man named Bill, but he looked as destitute as any of the other addicts whom he might meet on the streets. In fact, that was where David met him, in a derelict tenement building in the Bronx that was used by junkies.

Bill arrived on the doorstep of Clinton Avenue a couple of weeks later. Unlike the kids who usually visited the Center, he would only talk about the wonders of modern medicine and how his father's doctor friends would help him. It was as if money would solve everything.

David was also shocked by the way in which Bill's parents reacted when they heard about his addiction. They didn't seem very interested in Bill's current predicament. All they wanted to do was convince David that they weren't to blame. They had given Bill everything he could have possibly wanted, everything that money could buy. If he had problems now, it wasn't their fault. He must have got in with the wrong crowd.

Bill wasn't like the other addicts, they argued. And they pressed this point so forcefully that they persuaded David to let Bill go home before he'd finished the first stage of withdrawal, even though this was not usually allowed.

The results were tragic. Bill never did manage to come off drugs completely, in spite of several stays at the Center. Fourteen months after his first visit, he died of an overdose on a Harlem rooftop. David was asked to break the news of his death to his parents.

They wouldn't even come to the morgue to identify him.

`Please, will you take care of it, Reverend? Let us know if there's anything to pay . . .'

At that time not many people knew that suburban teenagers were getting involved with drugs. But David realized that the problem would soon reach epidemic proportions. It wouldn't be too long before Teen Challenge Centers were looking after more and more middle-class addicts, and they simply wouldn't be able to handle the problem on such a widespread scale.

The problem was that the Mafia was recruiting addicts faster than Teen Challenge could save them, and each addict would have to recruit two or three others to get enough money to feed the habit. Each of those would in their turn recruit another two or three as well. With this sort of progression, it wouldn't be too long before a couple of thousand new addicts had been created.

David was at a loss to know what to do. There had to be some way of halting this terrible epidemic, yet he couldn't imagine what it would be. But unknown to him, something was happening in New York to combat the menace of drug addiction.

He found out about it quite by chance one day in Manhattan when he was working on the streets alone. He was surprised to see that he didn't seem to be coming across as many drug addicts as usual.

He got talking to a young black boy and explained to him the sort of work he was doing on the streets of New York.

`I've noticed that there don't seem to be as many junkies around these days,' remarked David.

`Around here the word's out,' replied the boy. `Speed kills.'

His words took David by surprise. It was a message he, the police and health professionals had been trying to get across for years. But here it was coming from the mouth of an ordinary boy from the streets.

`And as for H,' continued the boy. `H ain't

cool. I don't want those Brown Berets giving me a hard time.'

Later, David thought about the conversation and it eventually dawned on him what the boy had been talking about. The kid had been telling him off for daring to suggest that he might be on drugs.

But what did it mean when he said `The word's out'? And what did the Brown Berets have to do with all this? All he knew about them was that they were a group of militant black and Puerto Rican New Yorkers.

David did a bit of subtle investigating in some of the shadier parts of town and found out that the Brown Berets were now campaigning fiercely against drugs. According to them, drug addiction was just a new way of turning black people into slaves and pushers and addicts were to be despised.

It was a very interesting discovery. Here were some members of the community working, not to cure addiction, but to prevent it. And according to the records kept by Teen Challenge, the Brown Berets' efforts seemed to be paying off. If only he could follow their example and get teenagers everywhere to spread the word that drugs were bad news!

It was a great idea, but the hard part was knowing how to turn it into reality. To make a real difference in America would require the cooperation of a lot of young people. Where were they going to come from?

He was to find the answer to that question much sooner than he imagined.

CHAPTER FOURTEEN

`What about us?'

The letter was postmarked Phoenix, Arizona.
David opened it and unfolded the piece of paper
inside. It was an invitation for him to hold a
rally there. Nothing unusual about that – he
received many such invitations – but somehow
this one was different. He didn't understand
why, but this particular one seemed to stand out
from the others.

`Is this what you want, Lord? Am I to go to
Phoenix?' he asked.

Yes, he was. It felt as if the Lord wanted him
to meet someone there.

The rally in Phoenix was more dramatic than
most. Moved by the testimony of a young
minister who had confessed he had been involved in the occult, many young people came to the
front to renounce their involvement in occult
practices. They were joined by several addicts
who wanted to give up the alcohol or drugs they
depended on.

Watching these people reach a turning point
in their lives was a moving experience, but
David felt he hadn't yet encountered the person
God intended him to meet.

Just before the meeting closed, a teenage girl
made her way to the platform where David was

sitting. She wanted to say something. David was intrigued. She looked like a sensible, respectable girl. Surely she didn't have any dark secrets to confess?

`I'd like to say something, please, Mr Wilkerson.'

She was pleasant in her manner, quite different from the troubled, aggressive teenagers David did so much of his work with. She took her place at the microphone and spoke, quietly but firmly.

`We've heard a lot this evening about addiction, homosexuality and the occult. These are big problems, I know, and like you I give thanks for everything that God has done to help people overcome them.'

She paused, and she was looking slightly embarrassed. `But I don't have any of these big problems, so it seemed as if you were missing me out – me and hundreds of others like me. We don't drink. We don't take drugs. We aren't involved in devil worship.'

David sat up and listened carefully. This girl had a valid point.

`Yes,' she continued, `we do have problems which get in the way, so that we don't always stand up for what we believe. But compared to the problems that people have been sharing tonight, ours are nothing, so we keep them to ourselves. Sometimes we feel that nobody cares about us. It's as if we're forgotten teenagers.'

Forgotten teenagers. Those words stuck in David's mind. She had identified an important oversight in his ministry.

`Thank you very much for being so frank,' he said. `I appreciate what you said and I'll think very seriously about it.'

Afterwards, reflecting on her words, things that he had seen and heard started to fall into place. He knew of a girl who had told her friends that she was using heroin. It turned out that she had only said it to get attention, and she didn't even know the first thing about the drug. How sad it was that she needed to lie like that, he thought.

And he remembered, to his shame, how his own daughter had been reluctant to come and share a problem with him because she didn't feel it was serious enough to bother him with. She had gone to see her grandfather and talked to him about it instead.

Why should the bad kids get all the attention and the good kids get none? David decided to make sure that things didn't happen that way any longer.

He made his intentions public a few days later when he was appearing as a guest on a television chat show. The host asked him what his solution was to the growing drug problem in the suburbs.

`I think it's best if the youngsters hear an anti-drug message from people their own age,' he replied. `And the people to spread that message are the Forgotten Teenagers, the ones who don't take drugs and don't have major problems. I intend to use them.'

But David hadn't thought out the solution thoroughly, as his interviewer suggested afterwards when they were off the air.

`Why haven't these Forgotten Teenagers been spreading the antidrugs message already then?'

David thought back to the young girl at the rally and remembered what she had said. She had mentioned `problems that get in the way so that we don't always stand up for what we believe.'

He was beginning to understand what she had been getting at. If young people feel guilty about something they've been doing or thinking, how can they stand up for what they believe? They would feel like hypocrites.

At last David could see a way forward. Before he did anything else he had to find out what it was that was troubling these well-meaning teenagers. Because the small problems that were bothering them were as big a barrier to these kids as drug addiction was to others.

Every time David led a rally he saw this as an opportunity to do something for the country's Forgotten Teenagers. He began each address with a big thank you to all the young people who had resisted drugs, and he was delighted with the huge round of applause that usually followed. A climate was developing among Christians in which the Forgotten Teenager was valued. A young person no longer needed a serious problem to be noticed and appreciated.

He also used the rallies to find out about the young people's concerns by giving out thousands of questionnaires for them to complete. They didn't have to give their names if they didn't want to. The most important question, asked `What is your Number One problem?'

David and his helpers at Teen Challenge were able to collate the answers and divide the teenagers' worries into three categories. One night he and Gwen got together to discuss the results which were very interesting indeed.

First, it appeared that teenagers worried about things they did that they thought were wrong. They were particularly concerned about sex, drugs, alcohol and smoking. For example, a young person might be involved in a sexual relationship with someone but feel guilty about it. And some of them thought that if they were addicted to cigarettes they had no right to criticize someone else for using hard drugs?

Next on the list were their problems with relationships. Many of them found it especially difficult to get along with their parents. Sometimes they even hated them. They felt as if their parents didn't understand them or care about them. Others felt that their parents were too strict with them and criticized them too much. Often it appeared that parents and children just weren't able to communicate with one another.

Their final major worry was what was going to happen to the world and mankind in the future. This was such a huge one that it often depressed them and made them feel like giving up on life. There seemed to be so many serious threats to the survival of the world – natural disasters, ecological problems, atomic warfare, the population explosion, to name but a few.

`They're tough problems,' said Gwen when David had finished describing the young people's concerns.

`They certainly are,' said David. `There's no way I can give these young people answers to them at the moment. All I can do is pray for wisdom and trust that the Lord will guide me.'

It took David months to find solutions to the teenagers' problems. The first one he tackled was their wrongdoing. He prayed fervently for God to show him what he ought to do to help them.

The answer he got was that it is impossible to help anyone unless they are desperate and really want to stop behaving in a particular way. People can only change if they really want to. But even if they do want to change, there is no way they can overcome their bad habits on their own. Turning over a new leaf is not the answer if a person doesn't have the inner resources to make it work. Real freedom comes when people put their trust in God and expect miracles to happen.

When David started teaching these simple principles, he found that they really were effective. Many of the young people reported that they were finally making breakthroughs in areas of their life that had been causing them difficulty.

He also told the young people that God would be able to take away the hatred from their relationships and replace it with love. After all, God had promised in the Bible that He would renew people's relationships. But when it came to dealing with their parents, it might be better if they conveyed their love in actions rather than words, by doing some chores round the house, for example.

The preacher found that he did have a well thought out answer to the teenagers' worries about the fate of the world and humankind. Every time he heard about disasters or threats to humanity, he related them to predictions in the Bible about the End Times. They were signs that Jesus would be returning soon to bring about a new world order.

David knew that this was a very complicated and controversial subject, and Christians often discussed it in high-faluting language. But after talking to one particular teenager, David realized that young people needed a clear and simple explanation of the Second Coming.

One thirteen-year-old boy named Bobby was very worried about what was going to happen to the world. He didn't see any point in going to school because, the way things were going humankind would soon blow the world to smithereens. His beliefs were making him depressed and sapping his energy.

So David wrote a letter to Bobby explaining very simply what would happen in the Second Coming. Not everyone would agree with the explanation that he gave, but it was the one which was favoured by David's church and other churches adopted a similar approach to Christianity.

Understanding the Second Coming would motivate the teenagers, he thought, and jolt them out of their resignation. If Jesus was going to come and separate the righteous from the unrighteous, they would need to make sure they were ready for him. They also ought to tell other people what was going to happen so that they could prepare themselves as well.

So David had found answers to the young people's three biggest hang-ups, and as he began to share them he found they were having the desired result. The teenagers now had the inner strength to stand up and tell their friends that it wasn't worth getting involved with drugs. David now had a new army of ambassadors for the cause who were ready and willing to spread their message with power and conviction.

But while the young people grew stronger and more able to minister, David found that he himself now had a personal problem which was crippling him and causing a great deal of stress in his life. It was even affecting his health.

The focus of David's own ministry had gradually been shifting as the months had passed. He now saw his main role as that of freeing young people from the things that were holding them back in their Christian lives. David's brother, Don, now dealt with the bulk of the administrative work at Teen Challenge, leaving David free to travel and encourage the young people. These days David was flying a hundred thousand miles a year to South America, Africa and Europe, as well as to various parts of North America.

His big problem was that he was petrified of flying. He could never relax and enjoy a flight because he was always convinced that something dreadful was going to happen. Every time he went up in an aeroplane, his imagination worked overtime thinking about all the things that might go wrong.

Over the years he had tried everything he could think of to get rid of his fear of flying. He had prayed about it. He had fasted. He had asked other people to pray for him. He had even taken flying lessons. But nothing ever seemed to work.

Even a pleasant, uneventful flight was an ordeal for David, and if a problem did occur, he was turned into a nervous wreck. Once he was about to fly from Los Angeles to Tulsa, but the rear engine caught fire and the pilot had to make an emergency landing. David was beside himself with fear. His worst nightmare had nearly come true.

A fortnight later the preacher was again on a flight, to Tampa, only this time the plane had to land in the middle of a hurricane. The landing was so rough that some passengers screamed and even the stewardesses had lost their usual composure.

All this stress was beginning to take its toll on David's body. Like his father, he had a tendency to stomach ulcers. He found this traumatic, not just because of the physical pain involved, but also because it brought back to him distressing memories of his father screaming in pain when he was ill for the last time.

David's father had died of his ulcer and David was determined he would never allow his own family to see him suffering like that. He watched his diet and took whatever medicines his doctor prescribed for him, but it wasn't enough. One day David collapsed at home and had to be rushed to hospital in an ambulance.

He was placed in intensive care and given various tests and X-rays to find out what exactly was the problem. The results showed he had a duodenal ulcer in exactly the same place as his father's had been.

`Will I have to have an operation?' he asked, praying that the doctor would say no.

`Let's see if you can get by without one by adjusting your diet. I'll give you some medication as well.'

David was relieved. At least his family would be spared the worry of an operation.

The doctors were working on the physical symptoms of his stress, but the cause of it remained. He still had to fly, and he still found flying a traumatic experience. His fear was compounded by guilt, for he felt that he ought to be able to overcome his problem. How could he tell other people that God would cure them of their drug addiction when his life was being ruined by a phobia ?

By now he was becoming very sensitive about his problem and would fly off the handle if any of his staff made a remark about his fear of flying. He was angry with them for reminding him of it and angry with God for not answering his prayers and curing him of it.

On one of his flights he discovered that his old friend Dr Ward was also on the plane. Dr Ward was a devout Christian and pastor whom David admired greatly. He went over and sat beside him and tried his best not to show how scared he was.

The two men got talking and eventually David confessed that he was terrified of flying.

`How can you sit here so calmly?' he said to Dr Ward. `I wish you'd tell me your secret. I've tried everything to overcome this awful fear.'

`Tell me, David, are you afraid of dying?' asked Dr Ward.

`I don't think so,' said David. `I've been in some pretty dangerous situations with people threatening to kill me, but no, I was never this scared.'

`So what is it that bothers you then?'

`I suppose it's the fear of falling.'

`That's it, then. It's a sort of structural weakness that you have.'

`Something that's inbuilt, you mean?'

Dr Ward explained that he was claustrophobic and couldn't even bear to sit between two people on a platform. Like David, he had tried to overcome his phobia by prayer and fasting, but nothing made any difference.

`Remember how St Paul talked about his ``thorn in the flesh''?' said Dr Ward. `Well, maybe your fear of flying and my claustrophobia are like that. Weaknesses in the way we're made that we're never going to overcome.'

That was something new for David to think about, and it did reassure him a little, but unfortunately it didn't stop his ulcer from giving him pain. He carried on flying as usual and putting up with the pain until something happened that he couldn't ignore.

David was making a journey back from British Columbia and the rest of the team had persuaded him against his better judgement to travel by air. That way they would only have a half-hour flight instead of a two hour trip by ferry.

The plane was a small commercial one, and when they hit a bad storm it was tossed about all over the place. The lightning flashes seemed very close and the roar of the thunder sounded deafening. Because David was petrified, his ulcer was killing him, but most of the passengers were just eating and drinking as usual, and they didn't seem at all concerned by the storm.

Then suddenly the plane fell a thousand feet. The air stewardess who was handing out drinks found herself on the floor and the drinks and glasses went everywhere. Some of the female passengers shrieked and all the babies on board started to bawl.

To David's relief, the plane managed to land in Seattle, but they were put onto a second plane which had an equally rough flight. David was clutching his stomach in agony by the time he eventually got out at the airport and he swore he would never fly again unless it was absolutely necessary. For once, his colleagues didn't argue with him. They had found the journey pretty nerve-racking too.

But David's decision not to fly came too late. His ulcer was in a very bad state by now and he had to call the doctor.

`Mmmm, I'm afraid this time there's no two ways about it, David. You're definitely going to need an operation.'

Strangely enough, it was in the hospital's recovery room after his operation that David began to conceive of a solution to his problem. A verse from Scripture came into his mind as he lay there. It was from the First Epistle of St Paul to the Corinthians, chapter ten. The verse was a reminder that God won't allow anyone to be tempted so much that they can't cope with it. It promised that God would provide a way of escape if the temptation seemed too much to bear.

God had promised a way of escape! That must mean that there was something David could do to avoid all the stress and pain that flying caused him.

The answer came to him immediately. He thought that it might not be very fashionable in a society where people use planes all the time, but from now on he was going to travel on a bus of his own.

But then he thought of a practical problem. Living on the east coast and doing a great deal of his work on the west coast meant that he would waste a lot of time sitting on the bus, being driven across the continent.

Straightaway, the Lord seemed to give him the other part of the answer. It was very simple. He would move to Dallas.

`But Lord, what about the people I work with? What about New York?'

`You can take your staff with you to Dallas,' came the response. `And remember that I called you to work with people, not with places. You must move to Dallas.'

David could hardly wait to tell Gwen. She took the news very calmly.

`I had a feeling something like this was going to happen. I've been telling the children that their lives were going to change soon. Now I know why.'

Gwen's hunch seemed to confirm the decision he had made, but David wanted to make extra sure he was doing the right thing, so he asked the Lord for a token of goodness, just as King David did in Psalm 86. It would show that he was doing what the Lord wanted.

David chose the name of a building firm from the classified advertisements and went along to meet the builder. He was amazed by the warm welcome he was given when he introduced himself.

`I've been waiting many years to meet you,

Mr Wilkerson,' said the builder. `Just let me know what you want.'

`I'd like a floor plan for an office,' replied David.

The builder and his architects got together with David that afternoon and sketched out the floor plan exactly the way he wanted it. Then when David got round to talking about the money he would need to pay for the building and buy himself a bus, the builder offered to introduce David to the bank manager. The bank manager then offered him seventy-five thousand dollars' credit without David even having to make a down payment.

Looking back on the events of the day, David saw that the Lord had generously provided him with two tokens of His goodness. This strengthened his resolve to make the move to Dallas. He wouldn't have to fly nearly so often, and life suddenly looked a whole lot better.

The decision turned out to be a good one. Not only did it save David a lot of pain and anxiety, but by revising his schedules, he now found he had a lot more time at home. The bus was a much more flexible method of transport as he could now travel at the times that he wanted rather than having to stick to the airlines' schedules. What's more, he could stop the bus and stretch his legs whenever he felt like it.

Travelling expenses were halved, a bonus

which he hadn't anticipated. And instead of
sending books and leaflets on separately, he
could take them with him on the bus.

All in all there were many advantages in
David's new way of working. He was still
scared of flying, but now that he didn't have to
do it so often it didn't blight his life in the same
way. God had provided him with a way of
escape, and he was very, very grateful for it.

CHAPTER FIFTEEN

Pastures new

`Well, here we are, Gwen, said David. `We've finally arrived at Lindale and we have everything we need – somewhere to live, an office and a bus.'

Gwen smiled at her husband. It was remarkable how easily things had fallen into place. They certainly seemed to be in the place where God wanted them.

`It looked as if we were taking a huge step by leaving New York and starting again here,' continued David. `But the Lord took care of everything and things seem to be working out really well. I wonder what new challenges He'll have for us here.'

David was right to think that his move to pastures new would bring with it new challenges and new experiences. No longer was he focusing his energies on New York and the problems of the inner city. His was now a travelling ministry, for he would go to any church or group that invited him, whether it was in the United States or the wider world.

Of course he had already been travelling for some time, but he'd been trying to maintain his involvement with Teen Challenge as well by remaining in New York. It was like trying to live in two worlds at the same time.

Now he was firmly committed to his travelling ministry and he was able to take a much more sensible approach to the practicalities involved. There would be no more flying for him unless it was absolutely necessary!

Lindale was now the headquarters for his ministry, but the Teen Challenge headquarters remained in New York. For the crusades and campaigns that he went on, David had his own team of back-up staff and road people based at Lindale who looked after the administration and organization and accompanied him on his travels.

Lindale also was to be the home of a new organization which David founded, World Challenge. It was conceived as a nonprofit-making religious corporation which aimed to provide funds for social projects throughout the world.

World Challenge sent out information on a regular basis to its many supporters to keep them informed about the work it was sponsoring. It wasn't difficult for the organization to build up a huge army of adherents. After all, many people knew about David through the film or book of *The Cross and the Switchblade*, through crusades or through books and articles. Most of the people on the mailing list were keen to help him with his work praying for him or donating money towards projects. The World Challenge mailing list grew steadily until it eventually included over three hundred and fifty thousand people.

One of David's projects was to set up a training centre in Lindale for former addicts who wanted to work in rehabilitation programmes. Although he was no longer working at Teen Challenge, he was still very much committed to the type of work it did and cared deeply about people of all ages who were trying to rebuild their lives after squandering precious months and years on drug or alcohol abuse.

David now spent a large proportion of his time on the road, but he also had quieter spells where he was able to stay at home and be more reflective. Writing books was another aspect of his ministry that was growing in importance. He found that the solitude of writing offered a valuable respite from his hectic life as an evangelist.

One of David's books caused a storm in religious circles when it was first published. For quite some time David had been convinced that it is vital for Christians to understand the Second Coming and prepare themselves for it. He had tried to explain this complicated doctrine very briefly and simply in his 'Letter to Bobby', something which he wrote to one of the many teenagers he met who were worried about the future of the world.

But now he expounded his views at greater

length in *The Vision*, which was published in 1974 and caused a sensation among Christian circles, partly because David was already such a well-known figure in American life, and partly because it was controversial.

In this prophetic book David predicted that many dreadful events would happen including earthquakes in the United States and climatic changes and famines worldwide. The preacher warned that American society was under threat as marijuana would one day be legalized and many more teenagers would become alcoholics. The nation would be deluged with pornography and there would be a rise in sexual immorality including rapes by homosexual gangs.

He had stern warnings for the churches too. According to David, there would be sexual immorality among the churches' ministers. He also foresaw the growth of a superchurch which would rise to a position of world prominence.

It wasn't easy for David to write *The Vision* and face up to what might happen when it was published. He was a highly respected figure, an authority on drug addiction and a world-famous evangelist, yet here he was producing a book which some people might regard as cranky. At the very least his tales of doom and gloom were sure to offend many ordinary churchgoers and pastors as well as people from many sectors of American society.

But how could he not have written the book?

After all, the important thing, David believed, was not whether the public admired you or churchpeople liked you. What really mattered was staying faithful to God and obeying His commands. He had prayed long and hard about the book and he honestly believed that this was the message that God wanted him to pass on. But perhaps the publication of the book was the first indication that he was finding himself out of kilter with the mainstream churches?

David's travelling ministry brought him into contact with countless members of the clergy and numerous congregations all over America. And the more he saw of church life in the United States, the more it disturbed him. Time and time again he came to the conclusion that pastors were not doing their duty to God and to their flocks.

It seemed to him that some ministers of religion didn't want to rock the boat, so if church members were doing something wrong they wouldn't speak out against their wrongdoings as forcefully as they ought to. Ministers were also reluctant to discipline their own families when family members went astray.

David felt very strongly that this lax behaviour was not what God wanted from His people. If Christians were doing wrong, if they were gossiping or having sex before marriage or having affairs, the pastor must condemn their behaviour clearly and unambiguously. In his opinion, many pastors had become far too soft.

`I can't understand it,' he said to Gwen one day. `It's as if they're frightened to speak out against sin. They aren't doing their duty.'

`Maybe they're frightened they'll drive away their congregations,' said Gwen. `You know how many people are drifting away from the churches these days. If a pastor's congregation takes exception to what he says and lots of members leave his church, he might find himself out of a job.'

`But that's the whole point,' said David. `I believe the reason people are leaving the church is because it's become too wishy washy.'

He sighed, remembering some of the things he'd seen and heard on his travels. `Some of the clergy have been watering down Christianity so much that it's become unrecognizable. Their congregations never really hear the word of God. They're never really confronted with the truth.'

David felt that the Church was becoming far too worldly in its outlook and its behaviour. That was why young people were becoming disillusioned with it and getting involved in drugs or sex instead. It was because they didn't see any evidence of God's power in the churches they attended.

`It's all very well having lots of singing and praise in church services, but these pastors are neglecting the word of God. They aren't providing good, solid biblical teaching. Without that, a lot of what goes on in church is just froth. People go along on a Sunday to enjoy themselves, not to hear what God has to say to them. In fact, they'd be very surprised if God said anything to them at all.'

`So why have the churches got into that state?' asked Gwen.

`I think it must be the fault of the pastors. You wouldn't believe some of the pastors I've seen. They're so busy thinking about how they can get a more prestigious church or make more money for themselves that they don't even consider what God wants. Some of them have been backsliding for so long they're no longer able to preach with conviction and others have drifted into lives of immorality.'

Gwen nodded. She'd been shocked by some of the things that she'd heard about pastors having affairs. She could understand that a man might be tempted to stray from time to time, but a pastor ought to be able to resist temptation. Some of these people seemed to have no shame.

`You know,' continued David, `if God wants to do marvellous work today, I don't think he'll do it through the clergy. They're all washed out. Only a few of the clergy and the laity are responsive. I guess we're God's new remnant.'

Yes, the churches were in trouble, but at least David felt he was doing what he could by pursuing his evangelistic work. `I'll keep on doing this, Lord, just as long as it's what You want of me,' he promised.

The fate of the nation was still a great concern of David's, and in 1985 he had another book on this subject published. It was entitled *Set the Trumpet to thy Mouth* and in it he prophesied that the United States would be wiped out in an atomic war. It would be God's terrible judgement on the nation for rejecting Him.

David spent many hours in prayer grieving for the state of the world and the Church. It was as if he was the only one who could see what a desperate situation they were in, and that was an extremely lonely position to be in.

At other times, though, he rejoiced at how fortunate he was, for his life in Lindale was extremely happy. He and Gwen lived in a beautiful house right beside a lake and they were extremely fond of it. There was no doubting now that the couple loved each other and were happily married, even though Gwen's cancer was still proving to be a trial for both of them. There was a lot of pain in her life, and she had to undergo operation after operation. It was difficult for David to have to watch her suffer when there was nothing he could do to help her. But at least nowadays they supported each other, and this gave them strength.

David was delighted when, after ten years in Texas, the Lord called him to go back and spend the summer months working on the streets of

New York. He felt a deep spiritual connection with the city and he was glad to put his experience and knowledge of it to good use. The summer street work was very successful and it became an annual fixture in his diary.

As the years passed, David began to think more and more about retirement. He hadn't burned himself out and he still enjoyed his work, but he had, after all, been working hard for nearly thirty years, ever since he first went to New York to set up Teen Challenge. Surely he deserved a rest by now ?

He wasn't quite sure how he would spend his retirement. Maybe he would move to Colorado and devote more of his time to writing. Or perhaps he would go and find some new work to do in Eastern Europe. The idea appealed to him and it would certainly be very interesting.

Whatever he eventually decided upon, he was sure that life in retirement would be a little easier than it had been for the last few years. He had found it stressful travelling around so much, even by bus, and he was getting a bit old to walk the New York streets. And Gwen's illness had been tough on both of them as well. Yes, it would be good to retire and enjoy living life at a slower pace.

At least, that's what David thought. But one of his summer visits to New York was to throw him into a state of turmoil yet again.

After many years of ministering to the most

desperate and deprived inhabitants of New York, David thought he had seen the worst that the city had to offer. Drugs, alcohol, sex, violence, nothing could shock him now, or so he told himself.

But in the summer of 1986 he began to realize that New York City had plumbed new depths of depravity which were much, much worse than anything he had witnessed previously in all his years at Teen Challenge.

Why had the city degenerated to such a level? The answer was simple. It was the arrival on the scene of crack, a drug deadlier than heroin. Crack addiction was spreading at an alarming rate in the city and nobody was immune to it. There were twelve-year-olds pushing the drug and even some clergymen were turning into crack addicts.

Even fear of dying didn't deter people from experimenting with the drug. In fact, David was horrified to hear one of the pushers announce, `I've got some of the stuff that killed Len Bias.' Len Bias was a famous basketball player who had died because of crack, but his death was seen as just another excuse to sell more of the substance that had killed him. The crack dealers were dealing in death and doing it quite blatantly.

David was hanging around Eighth Avenue one day, minding his own business and praying quietly to himself, when suddenly an odd-looking man came up to him. Using a torrent of foul language, he told David that he was interfering and warned him that his presence was not welcome.

`Get out of New York City. I'm warning you, get right out of here as quick as you can.'

On another occasion he saw someone snatch a baby from her mother in the middle of Manhattan's crowded 51st Street. He reacted quickly. `Stop that man! He's stealing a baby,' he yelled as he ran after the kidnapper, dodging passers-by who got in the way. Some youths joined in the chase with him, and eventually they caught up with the man.

David handed over the kidnapped baby to its mother. He expected she'd be grateful, relieved to get her baby back safe, or perhaps hysterical with worry after what she'd just gone through. Instead, she looked at him with eyes filled with hatred.

`Get out of here,' she screamed. `I know you. You don't belong in this city.'

David thought the woman's perverted reaction showed the extent to which evil was pervading the city.

There were other signs of New York's moral decay as well. When David lived in New York before, there had been homelessness, drug addiction and violence, but now it was on an even bigger scale. Young boys and girls were living on the streets, earning their living as

prostitutes. There were live sex shows, pornography and America's newest and most terrible
scourge, AIDS.

New York was like hell on earth.

What was needed was for one of the churches
to take a lead and fight to stop the moral and
spiritual deterioration that was wreaking havoc
in the city. But David had visited several of the
local churches and, on reflection, he sadly came
to the conclusion that they were not going to be
up to the task.

Many of the congregations had shrunk in size
so that they now consisted of only thirty to fifty
people. Their pastors were exhausted and
disillusioned after years of trying to minister in
the inner city with all its problems and
frustrations. It was obvious that they weren't
going to be strong enough to wage a battle
against evil and win it.

One night in August 1986, David was taking a
late night stroll in New York, in the Times
Square area, the city's theatre district. It was one
of the most famous areas in the world. Every
New Yorker was familiar with it, and many
people from other parts of America and other
continents had heard of it and visited it.

But as well as glamorous theatres and night-
clubs, there were also streets littered with
homeless people who ranted and raved like mad
things. There were crack addicts, drug dealers,

pimps, prostitutes and alcoholics. There was filth and squalor and crime and danger. In this area even the police cowered in their cars, afraid to step out into the blackness of the night, believing the situation was so dire that nothing they did would make a difference.

David could hear traffic noises, the hooting of car horns, the incoherent muttering of a down-and-out and aggressive shouting from some young men who seemed to be itching for a fight. The heavy smell of exhaust fumes filled his nostrils, mingling with the stench of stale beer and urine. And despite the garish glare of the neon lights which flashed above him, the blackness was almost tangible.

Tears came to his eyes. What hope was there for New York City? What future was there for a city so full of sin?

Slowly he made his way back to his hotel, his heart heavy with grief. He was mourning New York, this place which he loved so dearly, which had become so wicked and corrupt. He could see clearly that Times Square was the very heart of the city, where the battle between good and evil was being waged most fiercely. To save New York, someone would have to bring the light of Christ to Times Square. The question was, `Who?'

He turned the key and let himself in to his hotel room. It was one a.m.

'Please, Lord,' he begged, 'there is so much sin here. Please take pity on New York and raise up a church in Times Square.'

He heard a voice saying 'You know the city, David. You go and do it.'

CHAPTER SIXTEEN

Standing room only

Gwen knew what David was going to say even before he opened his mouth.

`We're going back to New York, aren't we?'

David shrugged his shoulders. `I don't know, honey. That's how it would seem at the moment, but I need more time to pray about this. A lot more time.'

Back home in Lindale, David cancelled all his appointments and spent day after day praying for the Lord to take pity on New York. He was listening for the Lord's voice, trying to discern His will. Everything else in his life came to a standstill. All that mattered to him right now was to spend time alone with God. This period in his life was like his own personal testing time, an experience that he had to go through to be purified and ready for the work that awaited him.

There were so many thoughts in his head, so many motivations jostling with one another, some good, some bad. How could he be sure that the Times Square Church wasn't just another of his crazy notions, like Kids Town had been? Was it just another way of glorifying himself? And if it wasn't, why did he have to take it on ? Surely there was another pastor who could go and set up a new church?

Then there was Gwen to think of. She'd been so ill, and she was happy here in her beautiful house by the lake. Was it fair to drag her back to the stresses of the city, to take on a demanding job which would mean there would be less time left for him to be with her? He knew she would be supportive about moving back to New York, but really, she didn't deserve all this upheaval.

And he thought about what it would entail to set up a church in Times Square. Land was expensive in Manhattan. It sold by the square foot. He reckoned it would cost millions for an auditorium that would be large enough to house a growing church.

He remembered the first Teen Challenge Center and how they had had to pray for every cent they needed. Every time a bill came in, they never knew how they were going to pay it. Would Times Square be like that all over again, only with much larger sums of money to find – impossibly large sums of money?

As he thought and prayed about this new challenge, images and memories kept flashing into his mind of the terrible sights he had seen during his visit to New York, and he cried and cried till his eyes hurt. What else could he do in the face of such ungodliness? New York was a city hell-bent on destroying itself.

He felt deep down that God would not allow

such sinfulness to continue indefinitely. God had made it clear what sort of behaviour he expected both from His Church and from society. By repeatedly breaking God's law, the people must surely bring judgement upon themselves.

`I want you to warn the city,' God told him. `Warn the people there of the judgement that is to come if they continue with their wicked ways.' But it was a hard message to be entrusted with, and David struggled against it.

However, the preacher could also see that God had positive plans for the city. Most of the churches didn't seem to care about the world's spiritual needs and were confused in their thinking. But God was now asking David to find the holy remnant, those few people who remained true to Him, and build them up so that Christians could have a real impact on the city.

As the months went by, God seemed to provide David with answers to the many questions that were troubling him. The preacher was told he wasn't to worry about the practicalities involved in moving to New York because everything would be taken care of. For a start, he would have all the helpers he needed. He wouldn't have to tackle this mission on his own as he feared.

The first two helpers David enlisted were his brother Don and a fellow minister of his named Bob Phillips. He described to them how he had felt after seeing New York again and he was delighted to find they felt the same way and wanted to be involved in the project. As they talked, the idea came to them that the three of them could form a ministry team to share the work and leadership of the new Times Square church.

David's other big concern, money, didn't seem so important either. God had reassured him that he wouldn't lack for money, and David believed Him, even though he couldn't see exactly where it was going to be coming from.

Finding suitable premises for the church might be difficult, but God promised that He would provide a magnificent building in Times Square to house His new church. When David saw it, it would take his breath away, for the new church would be more beautiful than he could ever have imagined.

After three months of agonizing soul-searching, David knew what the Lord wanted of him and he was ready to obey Him. No matter how difficult it would be, he was going to move to New York and set up a new church with the help of Don and Bob.

There was still one problem. The church that God was going to raise up through him in Times Square was for the faithful remnant. God was displeased with the existing churches and the way they were behaving. The new church would have to be nondenominational and independent. But David was still a minister with the

Assemblies of God, as he had been for the whole of his career.

With some sadness he resigned his ministerial position with the Assemblies of God. It was the end of a very long association with them, but he felt that God was calling him to make a new stand, and he had to obey, whatever the personal cost.

David moved to New York with Gwen, set up an office and looked for a building for the church to meet in. He soon found a suitable venue, and just a year after his late night stroll, he was launching the first of a series of meetings at the Town Hall, a concert hall and meeting room on 43rd Street, only a few yards from Times Square.

It would cost fifty thousand dollars to hire the hall for five meetings on four consecutive days. The price was high because the church would have to pay full theatrical rates for backstage services and lighting professionals. But the expenses were easily covered by donations sent in by people from the three hundred and fifty thousand address mailing list and money from supporters who attended the meetings.

David and his team had hoped to attract three hundred people to the first of the meetings, but, to his amazement, there was a packed house that night. Virtually all of the one thousand five hundred available seats were full, and the atmosphere was electric.

`I have something to tell you,' he told his attentive audience. `We're here to stay. We're here to stay.'

It looked as if the new church was getting off to a magnificent start if numbers were anything to judge by. In actual fact, many of the listeners who crammed into the meetings during that first week were already Christians who had spent a lot of time and money travelling from their homes in various states to be with him. They wanted to be with him at this important time to support him and show him that they were behind him one hundred per cent.

Eventually these supporters from out-of-town had to go home, and David and his co-workers were left to build up a congregation from scratch, no easy task in a city where congregations were dwindling all the time. Regular meetings started the following week, on Sunday mornings and evenings and Tuesday evenings. It was an encouragement to David that from the beginning New Yorkers attended them. As the word spread numbers rose rapidly, and it wasn't long before the Town Hall was packed, not just on special occasions, but week after week.

Things were going well, but the Town Hall was only ever intended to be a temporary home for the church, which was now known as Times Square Church. David was still looking for something more permanent, but he didn't feel he'd found the right premises yet.

After a while the church transferred to a nearby theatre, the Nederlander on West 41st Street. Many of the world's greatest plays had been premiered there, including *Who's Afraid of Virginia Woolf?* by Edward Albee and *The Little Foxes*, which starred the legendary Tallulah Bankhead.

As well as building up a congregation, David was also developing the church's outreach work. Teams were being sent out to work on the streets and Times Square Church was also sponsoring several outreach projects. One of these was Timothy House, a drug rehabilitation centre on the Lower East Side of town. The church also ran the Upper Room, a four room drop-in centre for the homeless, just across the road from the Port Authority bus terminal, and plans were being made to open a half-way house for girls.

The media were fascinated by the idea of the legendary David Wilkerson preaching to packed houses in a Broadway theatre. `A Times Square Church Gathers Rave Reviews' proclaimed *The New York Times*. The new church was certainly proving to be far more popular than David could ever have envisaged, and this was all the more remarkable because the Nederlander was situated in a particularly seedy side street.

After only three months of worshipping in its

new building, it was clear that the congregation had already outgrown the one thousand two hundred-seat Nederlander Theater. A bigger venue was urgently needed to house the church if it was to carry on growing to its full potential.

The church's rough location was also proving to be a problem for members of the congregation who were in danger of being mugged on their way to services, and every time someone parked their car outside the church they risked having it broken into or vandalized.

One day, the preacher had to stop the church service to announce that a yellow Mercedes belonging to a member of the congregation was being pushed away by some people outside the church. Another lady had her car stolen on one occasion and badly damaged on another while she was attending services. Somewhere safer would have to be found quickly for the Times Square members to worship.

About that time, David spotted in the newspapers that a show running at a nearby theatre had run into difficulties. It was a musical called *Legs Diamond* about a New York gangster in the twenties and it was playing at the Mark Hellinger Theater, just across the street from the Andrew Lloyd Webber show *Cats*.

The producers had envisaged that *Legs Diamond* would run for years and bring in millions of dollars, but unfortunately this particular production seemed to be dogged by bad luck from start to finish. The script had to be rewritten several times, a member of the cast was injured by the theatre curtain and critics gave the show appalling reviews.

The show's bad luck turned out to be good fortune for Times Square Church. This was just the lucky break it needed. If only the show would fold, there was a possibility that David could lease the Mark Hellinger and make it into the church's new home. The pastor prayed fervently for the speedy demise of *Legs Diamond* and even mingled with the disgruntled theatre-goers in the foyer to gauge the public's reaction to the show.

His prayers were answered. After only three months, *Legs Diamond* lowered its curtain for the last time and David was in a position to negotiate a five-year lease with the theatre's owners. Broadway productions were struggling at that time, so Times Square Church was in a strong position to take over the tenancy. It already had in the bank the one million dollars that would be needed for the first year's rent.

On March 12th, 1989, the Times Square Church opened in the Mark Hellinger Theater. It billed itself as `The Church that Love is Building', and right from the very first service it was a huge success. `Standing Room Only for Jesus on Broadway' announced one newspaper, while another proclaimed `David Wilkerson's Church a Broadway Hit'.

Remembering how uncertain he had been before he finally committed himself to coming to Times Square, David could see now that God had been true to His word. He had indeed provided David with a magnificent building for his church, for the Mark Hellinger Theater was the flagship theatre of Broadway. Many people believed that it had the most elegant auditorium in the whole of America. And entering the foyer, with its ornate gold columns, flowing gold curtains and plush red carpet was like walking into heaven.

Yes, God had provided a truly breathtaking home for His new church, He had given David workers to labour alongside him and He had supplied the money to run it, just as He had promised. It cost two hundred thousand dollars to get the Mark Hellinger ready for the move, but there had been no difficulty in finding the money. Everything David needed for his new ministry had been provided in abundance.

David's intuition had been right. Times Square, the heart of the city, was obviously the right location for the new church. It had an extremely high profile and nobody could fail to notice the tremendous impact it was having on New York City as a whole. The message was coming across loud and clear that there was now a strong Christian presence in the midst of the physical and moral decay of Broadway.

But what was perhaps most remarkable was

the wide range of people who flocked to the church week after week. Many of the worshippers were middle- and upper-class people from Manhattan, the Connecticut suburbs, Long Island and New Jersey. But alongside them, and making up about a third of the congregation, were drug addicts, prostitutes, homeless people, transvestites and AIDS patients. Men, women and children of many different ages, races and backgrounds, rich and poor sat side by side, united in Christ.

Times Square Church continued to flourish so that before it had even been in its new building for a year, three and a half thousand people already regarded it as their church and had registered their names on the church's computer cards. Many, many people had taken the church to their hearts and found it provided what they were looking for in life.

Having a large congregation to look after meant that David's ministry took on a new emphasis. No longer was he the roving evangelist who would spend a day or two in a town and then be gone. He wanted to be at all the church's services to show he was committed to his congregation. He had mellowed over the years and had turned into a kind and caring pastor. He regarded it as a great privilege to be able to get more closely involved with people and share in their joy and their pain.

The church's outreach work carried on ex-

panding. The planned half-way house for women and girls had become a reality. Hannah
House, a brand new apartment house, just one
street away from Times Square Church, aimed to
provide accommodation for Christian widows of
at least sixty years of age who would otherwise
be homeless or living in squalid conditions. It
would also help unmarried mothers and women
and girls who had problems in getting their life
under control.

Another of the church's projects was the
Raven Mobile Food Truck which took its name
from the raven that fed the prophet Elijah by the
river Cherith. The truck was kitted out with a
kitchen so that members of the church could
take food to the hungry and the homeless who
lived on the streets. It was able to provide
hundreds of homeless people with hot soup,
turkey hot dogs and coffee in the winter and a
tasty and nutritious pasta salad in the summer.

There was no doubt at all that Times Square
Church was reaching the most desperate and
troubled members of society, the very people
whom David had wept over as he took a late-
night stroll round the city in the summer of 1986.
The church was showing the world that the
gospel is preaching in action. By caring for the
poor and needy, it was demonstrating God's
love and concern.

David was happy to be at Times Square
Church looking after his thriving congregation,

but he also had to put up with hostility which became more intense as time went on. He was criticized by some of his fellow Christians who didn't like his confrontational approach to religion, and a Christian magazine accused him in an editorial of being divisive and presumptuous because he had denounced Christian rock music.

It seemed there would always be people who disliked what he was doing and would do anything they could to discredit him. One day David was sitting in a meeting with some people who didn't know who he was. When they found out he went to Times Square Church they said, `Do you know that David Wilkerson is divorced?' David introduced himself and reassured them that he and Gwen were enjoying a long and happy marriage, contrary to any rumours they might have heard.

David had personal problems to contend with as well. Gwen was continuing to have trouble with her health, and over the years she had numerous operations for cancer which left her with physical and emotional scars. But having suffered herself, she eventually found she was in a position to offer comfort and hope to women who wrote to her after finding lumps in their breasts or were undergoing mastectomies.

Even now Gwen is still seriously ill with cancer and is often in great pain. For months on end David has to survive on only three hours sleep a night because he is taking care of his wife. It is an immense strain for him to see her in agony, day after day, and he says he still doesn't understand why she must suffer so terribly. It breaks his heart that his two daughters have also had to battle against cancer and have undergone chemotherapy and radiation treatments for their illnesses.

When members of one's family are seriously ill, it is extremely stressful, so it is not surprising if David gets run down from time to time and finds that he cannot shake off colds and other minor illnesses as quickly as he ought to. He also has occasional days when tiredness lowers his spirits and he begins to wonder whether his wife and daughters would still be sick if only he had enough faith.

But most of the time he takes comfort in God's presence and finds in Him the strength to rise above his own worries and to minister with great power. During one of Gwen's recent bad spells, David stood up in church and preached, saying, `These last four months I've probably had three hours sleep a night, but I feel I could take on the world tonight.' And judging by the congregation's warm and enthusiastic response to his sermon, he certainly could.

The skinny preacher has come a long way since he hit the headlines during the Farmer trial, a naive young man from the country, unfamiliar with the violent streets of New York, but determined to do something, somehow, for seven young boys whose picture had haunted him.

Author of *The Cross and the Switchblade* and numerous other books, founder of Teen Challenge, the first in a worldwide network of two hundred drug rehabilitation centres, worldwide evangelist and now pastor of one of the newest and most exciting churches in the world, David Wilkerson has always stepped out into unknown territory with courage and determination. Time and time again, his bold ventures have had miraculous results.

But perhaps the key to all of these achievements, and his greatest success, is his overwhelming desire to stay close to God and carry out His will, however unlikely or impossible it might seem. He is truly a man of faith.

Who knows what the future may bring for David? When asked about his future plans for Times Square Church, David once said that he has no particular strategy for the church, no plans for its future. `The Lord will take it wherever He wants it.'

Throughout his life, that has always been true of David Wilkerson himself. The Lord has taken him wherever He wanted him. And we can be sure that whatever the future brings for David, whatever trials he may have to face, whatever new challenges await him, the skinny preacher will always be listening for the voice of the Lord and ready to follow His leading.